America, the
BEAUTIFUL?

Remember jigsaw puzzles you used to put together—ones that formed a mountain sunset, or fields of waving grain?

Famed author and ecologist George R. Stewart has assembled a different picture. **Its pieces are human excrement, beer cans, automobile exhaust, detergents, insecticides, smoke, heat, paper bags, industrial waste, and other familiar features of our landscape.**

And every day in every way that picture is getting bigger and bigger and bigger . . .

"The devastation which we have lazily, greedily, destructively inflicted on our own country. No more realistic horror story will be published. . . . Stewart makes it readable and concise; he places us against our vivid, reckless historical background; and he suggests responsible alternatives."—*The Atlantic*

SIGNET and MENTOR Titles
of Contemporary Interest

NOT SO RICH
AS YOU THINK

George R. Stewart

A SIGNET BOOK from
NEW AMERICAN LIBRARY
TIMES MIRROR

SIGNET TRADEMARK REG. U.S. PAT. OFF. AND FOREIGN COUNTRIES
REGISTERED TRADEMARK—MARCA REGISTRADA
HECHO EN CHICAGO, U.S.A.

SIGNET, SIGNET CLASSICS, MENTOR AND PLUME BOOKS
are published by The New American Library, Inc.,
1301 Avenue of the Americas, New York, New York 10019

FIRST PRINTING, AUGUST, 1970

PRINTED IN THE UNITED STATES OF AMERICA

Contents

1

HORROR STORY

WHEN SOME FUTURE HISTORIAN shall sit down to summarize what the present generation of Americans has accomplished, his climactic sentence could read, "Of the waters, they made a cesspool; of the air, a depository for poisons; and of the good earth itself, a dump where rats nuzzled in piles of refuse."

In the same stern mood he may write on: "Fixated upon the idea of production—even knowing their god as the Creator—they curiously forgot that everything thus produced must be either returned upon itself that the cycle could continue, or else must be given proper disposal. Instead, they cheaply polluted their environment—earth, air, and water—until there remained no decency of life. Their young men no longer fought bravely. For who dares his death willingly to defend a garbage dump? So, finally—seeing disorder and ugliness, drinking from tainted streams, breathing stench, and choking on fumes—as a people, they shriveled. And their land lay, for a while, desolate."

The American world gives some indication of ending in a bad smell. Moreover, we may definitely shift from the future to the present. The crisis is not about to arise; the crisis is here.

Such a claim, even in the recent past, might have seemed extreme and exaggerated. But in the past year, awareness of the situation has developed so rapidly that statements of impending disaster have become commonplace. Warnings have issued from high officials. On December 13, 1966, for instance, newspapers quoted both the Vice President and the Secretary of Health, Education and Welfare, to the effect that immediate disaster threatened from smog. On January 10, 1967, President Johnson in his State of the Union address stressed pollution as a critical problem for the nation, emphasizing befouled waters and smog-filled air. At the present date, therefore, any statement that the crisis has already arrived will be unlikely to cause argument, and may even seem to be the re-mouthing of an old phrase.

Much of the nightmare quality of the situation arises from mere bulk, whether expressed in cubic yards or in tons. One estimate has been made for the single item "urban solid wastes," that is, roughly, garbage and junk, as produced in cities. All things considered, it is one of the less pressing of the problems. But the horrifying conclusion is that each citizen of the United States, on the average, produces 1600 pounds of such materials a year. The annual total, therefore, is the figure, meaninglessly large for most people, of 125,000,000 tons. Merely to handle this material in our present halfhearted and inadequate manner, runs up a yearly bill of $2,500,000,000.

We may consider it no wonder that voices have already been raised to declare, "We are being buried in our own garbage!" Equally well, it can be put, "We are being smothered in our own fumes!" and, "We are being poisoned by our own effluents!" Civilization has trapped itself. . . .

The title of this book is apt and exact enough, though needing two words for expansion into: "You are not so rich as you think." The "you" means the citizens of the United States, taken collectively. Therefore, to some extent, that pronoun refers to each of the individual citizens. In a larger sense, also, it includes the inhabitants of the more highly civilized regions of the world.

All these people are thus living in more-or-less blissful ignorance of the true state of their finances because they have avoided paying current bills for "disposal." Collectively, they are like a family which has lived for many years in the same house without proper clean-up. Superficially these people took some pains. They swept the dust under the rugs, piled old newspapers in the corners of the living-room, and even carried some things to the attic and the basement. It was not too bad for a while. Eventually they were living in a slum, with mice, cockroaches, fleas, dust, and a foul odor. American civilization has arrived at that point.

Thus to arrive, we have allowed every year in our

accounting a hidden and unnoted, though sizable, item—the added degradation of the environment. In the grossest economic terms, we have not spent the money to clean up the mess. Instead, like the easygoing family, we have swept the mess under the rug, or just let it lie around.

We therefore face a double expense of many billions of dollars—to establish an effective current clean-up, and to take care of the accumulation of past years. The continuing charge will be an appreciable one in the whole national economy, a new and additional one. "Not so rich as you think."

This title, actually, was chosen before the book was written, and it has tended to seem somewhat inadequate—as the writer himself saw the situation more fully, and perhaps also as that situation itself worsened. The title was low-toned, where the conditions suggested something melodramatic. It seemed to write the problem off as one of dollars and cents, though politics, basic ways of life, and the status and habits of millions of individuals are involved. Science and technology also must be considered. Even granted knowledge, there still remains the question of motivation and self-discipline in a variously-minded people. There is the question whether some of the practices have already gone so far as to be irreversible. There is also—quite literally for many people, and even possibly for a civilization—the question of life and death.

Indeed, the title used for this first chapter might fittingly have served for the entire book—*Horror Story*. In the end, however, the low-toned title has been allowed to stand. Let the facts themselves do the screaming. . . .

The demonstration which is attempted here develops from two fundamental principles. . . . First, there is the elementary basic principle of science, to which most people have probably been exposed. It used to be called the Law of the Conservation of Matter, though physicists now prefer to put it "Mass," instead of "Matter."

But the law, though it may have been reworded, is still in effect. In the ordinary processes of nature, matter is not annihilated. It can pass from solid to liquid to gas and back again. At times it can even seem to disappear, as when water boils away. Still, according to the procedures of the workaday world, you cannot get rid of matter. You can transform it, hide it from sight, look away from it, bury your head in the sand, or adopt other devices—but you cannot destroy it.

The attitude of men—and even of civilized men—has failed to take into account this basic law. In disposing of sewage or garbage or anything else, people merely pushed it aside, as cheaply as possible, and seemed to hope that it would then disappear. In these recent years of crisis, the same people have been much surprised that these materials have not disappeared, but have piled up in larger and larger masses, sometimes transformed into something else, creating more and more deleterious effects. . . .

The second basic principle is that all disposal is essentially one problem. First of all, it is one politically. Nothing is gained in the long run if one city or county—or even one nation—merely casts off its refuse upon some other one, whether this procedure means sending smog into the air-currents, pouring sewage into a flowing river, or releasing atomic debris into the wind-driven atmosphere. Second, any fractionization of the elements of disposal is futile; they must be considered as one. It does no good, for instance, to get rid of garbage by burning if smog is thereby increased. Finally, the problem is one because there is only one environment. No matter where or from what the materials originate, they must be passed on into the same earth, water, and air.

Currently, the failure to grasp this unity is striking. Though scarcely a day passes without a story of some kind appearing in the newspapers, these accounts deal with one phase or another of the situation. One writer presents his story of mountains of garbage piling up in the outskirts of a city. Another tells of algae invading a previously crystal lake. A third one describes a river turned into liquid filth by factory effluents, manure from feeding pens, and raw sewage. A fourth and a twentieth, and a hundredth add their accounts of smog, pesticides, atomic residues, litter, and so on, in a seemingly endless and confused list.

The failure to recognize the unity is natural enough, for in its major aspects the problem is recent. People, therefore, recognize the parts without fitting them together into a whole.

One such evidence of recent development shows in the language itself. There does not exist in English—and perhaps not in any other language—any single traditional term covering the whole conception. Instead, we all know a host of more or less specific terms—*sewage, garbage, junk, litter, smog, refuse, waste, offal, slops, pollutants, rubbish, trash*. Many others exist, some of them not polite terms. There has even been a tendency in recent years to coin new words, such as *gook* and *gunk*.

Each of these words is useful, but not one of them is all-inclusive. Perhaps the nearest to universality is *crud*, that coinage of the G.I.'s of World War II. But that term is now old-fashioned slang, and in many people's minds approaches being an obscenity.

This book, therefore, must labor from its very beginning under this verbal lack. At least, the lack may indicate that this is a pioneer work.

Even the classification of the all-inclusive "it," the break-down into the component parts, is a matter of difficulty, without established precedent or sound definitions.

One frequent trial at classification is threefold, making a division into solids, liquids, and gases. This division is not very workable. The trouble is that most of the material has much water in it, and even is of a soupy nature, flowing like a lazy liquid but containing a heavy load of solids in suspension.

A more valuable classification for the ordinary citizen develops from the manner in which the material is handled, that is, whether it is primarily "committed" to water, land, or air. The qualification "primarily" allows for what happens after the processes of nature take over. Much material that is originally deposited on the land becomes water-borne with the first rainstorm. The processes of decay rapidly take charge of much that was land-committed or flushed into streams, and soon convert it into gases that mingle with the atmosphere. Soot that leaves the chimneys and ascends into the air drops back as a black deposit on the land. In many other ways too the interchange among the three "elements" is continual and wholly natural.

Still, the classification as to means of immediate disposal is a useful one, especially if it is combined with another. The secondary one, which follows common usage, rests upon the place and process of origin—its relation to civilization, that is, to daily life. Under the head of water-committed materials, in this secondary classification, come *sewage* and *factory effluents*. As land-committed, we have a heterogeneous group of five, comprising *garbage, junk, litter, agricultural refuse,* and *mineral refuse*. What is chiefly committed to the air falls under several heads, as *smoke, smog,* and the ultimate refuses, *carbon dioxide* and *radioactive wastes.*

This book—necessarily as an essay rather than as an exhaustive treatise—will attempt to present the whole problem. The next chapter sketches the historical background. Chapter 3 considers the immediate causes of the present crisis. Ten successive chapters, constituting the main body of the book, then discuss each of the main components—beginning with the water-committed, proceeding to the land-committed, and ending with those which are primarily committed to the air. Three final chapters then attempt to provide a conclusion—if not a solution.

2

DOWN FROM THE TREES

IN THE TREES there was no problem of disposal. How long man or man's ancestors thus lived arboreally, we have no certain way of telling. Several million years it may well have been. Certainly the period was long enough to establish basic ways of life.

The trees offered a built-in sanitation and refuse system. Whatever was discarded, it all fell neatly to the ground—excreta, nutshells, pods, hair-droppings. If, in these primitive years, there was such a phenomenon as a natural death, the dead body too, as its hands released hold, slumped off, fell, and disappeared. On the ground below, the humbler scavengers and the processes of decay soon dissipated all such materials and returned them to the soil.

By the time of the descent from the trees to the ground the hominoid had developed strongly fixed habits of non-concern about disposal. More bluntly, he was one of the dirtier animals. The wolf might keep his den neat. The wild ass might establish his latrine at a decent distance from the water-hole. But the hominoid, even though by then close to being man, continued in his old arboreal habit of unthinking nonchalance.

Indeed, during those early millennia of life on the ground the problem was not severe. Each band was small. Besides, though not necessarily nomadic, early man was wide-ranging. There was still no real problem of accumulation.

At some point in time, however, man began to inhabit fixed sites, such as dry and equable caves. Then through the years and centuries—to the immense delight of present-day excavating anthropologists—a rich deposit grew deeper and deeper, foot by foot, on the floor. Perhaps the adults drew a little aside for their needs, but certainly such conduct was not expected of small children. They squatted happily and unreproved among the decaying skins and bones of recent and more ancient kills.

The atmosphere of these caves must have grown to be richly redolent, but the varied odors were those of safety, comfort, and home. Eventually, if the stench became overpowering, the band could shift to another cave.

Again at some unknown point in time, arose the first beginnings of sanitation and disposal. The cause cannot have been a concern for public health or for aesthetics. More likely, such procedure arose from an early and animistic sense of religion, and the first disposals were of the dead.

Some strong man, let us say, was wounded in an encounter with a beast, and then dragged himself to the home-cave, and died there. The others began to feel an uneasiness, though not from the noisomeness of the putrefying corpse. Rather, as they looked at the staring eyes and grinning teeth, those still living were anxious and uncertain. Where had that strong spirit vanished? Did it still haunt the spot where its body lay?

If many caves were available, the easiest course was to abandon the old one and seek another. But eventually came a different solution—to carry the body away.

At first, doubtless, they merely laid the corpse anywhere, carelessly, for the beasts and the birds to devour. Or else they dumped it, for more security, into a cleft in the rocks and rolled stones upon it, to be sure that the spirit was kept down. Or, perhaps, they used the river, trusting to the crocodile. No matter what the method, man had begun a new era.

Late, unwillingly, and by makeshift methods, he had

faced the necessity of disposing of something which had once been useful and pleasant, but had come to be useless, unpleasant, and possibly dangerous.

Man has not yet advanced much beyond that point. As far as disposal is concerned, he may still be said to act, "late, unwillingly, and by makeshift methods." He continues to behave very much as if he still lived in the trees. Having pressed the lever on the toilet, dumped the garbage into the can, or thrown the beer can from the car window, he (or she) considers that act to be the end of personal responsibility . . .

Paleolithic man has left to us his shell-mounds and kitchen middens, but nothing to indicate that he was troubled by a problem of waste. He was much more concerned with getting a minimum to eat. Yet, at times, habitual famine must have yielded to occasional feast, in a time of good hunting. Then the decaying meat (no preservation being possible) must have fouled both the earth and the air of the camp ground. At such times, as scavengers, the wild dogs crept in to feed on the meat left by the cleverer hunter, and so, as anthropologists generally think, the alliance of man and dog first began.

Neolithic man, having invented living in permanent villages and keeping cows and sheep, immediately faced a disposal problem. This was one price of his advance toward civilization. Apparently he solved this problem by generally ignoring it.

His situation was approximately that of the agricultural peasant as it has existed over much of the world for many centuries, and still exists in some areas. The peasant lives in a village, usually a small one, where he huddles in with his animals. The animals increase the disposal problem several fold. Generally speaking, the peasant does not try to keep the village clean, but merely lives with the dirt.

The hunters and food-gatherers had known insecurity, but had at least enjoyed clean air and water, and even, much of the time, clean camp grounds. The agricultural peasant gained security with his fixed habitation and his animals, but he was forced always to live in the stinking filth. Of course, he could have cleaned it up; such work would not usually have been beyond his powers. But he had much labor to perform otherwise, and he was the inheritor of the old-time arboreal negligence. He found it easier to adjust to the dirt, until it became part of his life and the ammoniacal reek no longer bothered his nostrils.

Some thousands of years B.C. came the invention of the city. It differed from the village in many ways, in addition to being larger. It was not so closely tied to crop-raising and animal husbandry, but subsisted on food brought in from the villages. This food might be rendered as the tribute of a conquered people, or it might be given in exchange for manufactured goods or for military protection. Not having so many animals, the cities had a decided head start towards cleanliness. The earliest ones, indeed, like those of pre-Columbian America, may have had no animals at all except for a few dogs. Later, when asses and camels began to enter the cities as beasts of burden, some of the advantage was lost.

Otherwise, the cities had some disadvantages, especially in the greater numbers and concentration of people. Now, for the first time, there must have been the recognition of a "problem," and we can assume that the city fathers of several thousand years ago were making speeches as to what should be done about it.

Already there must have been the annoyance of the lazy and slovenly householder who allowed his premises to become noisome to his neighbors. Already there must have been the dilemma—whether to require, by law, that the citizen should dispose of his own filth, or whether it should be a municipal and tax-supported project. As has been true ever since, some municipalities handled the matter better than others did. Already in the third millennium B.C. the well-established and prosperous cities of Mesopotamia and the Indus Valley had sewers and drains, which later archaeologists have excavated with pleasure, and sometimes with wonder.

On the whole, however, ancient urbanites followed in the ways of their village ancestors, and were not much concerned at a little dirt, or even at a large amount.

Occasional cities, as digging reveals, were extraordinarily filthy. In a village you had at least been close to some place of disposal. But in a city, if you lived near the center, you had to carry everything clear out to the edge. This necessity meant a lot of work, and some people simply did not think it worth the trouble.

A remarkable case is furnished by one of the early cities at the site of Troy. Its people were some of the most lamentably bad housekeepers of all history. Their food-leavings (bones and everything apparently) they merely dropped on the floor, and went on living on top of them.

Naturally the floor-level rose, and eventually the door would not open. Then they merely adjusted the door!

On the whole, however, we know very little about the disposal methods of antiquity. Drains or sewers are rare, and archaeology does not reveal much, except about burials—and they are more religious in their connections than sanitary.

Ancient literature, dealing largely with heroic themes, is not concerned with sanitation. The Achaean camp at Troy doubtless had some arrangements, but Homer did not see the need of describing the latrine-system in hexameters.

Hesiod warned his readers against urinating in streams. Probably, however, he was not thinking in sanitary or aesthetic terms, but was considering that such an act would be an insult to the river-god—and such spirits were notoriously touchy, according to early Greek notions.

The Old Testament, so realistic in many of its details, does not get involved with disposal. There is the famous passage that each warrior should have a "paddle" on the butt of his spear so that he could cover up his own filth and not pollute the land. Though this regulation is attributed to Moses, there is no likelihood that it is much older than the text of Deuteronomy, about 700 B.C., and there is not, in fact, any evidence that the army of Israel actually observed that "law." Still, the mere mention of such an idea might be called forward-looking.

In Nehemiah, in connection with the rebuilding of Jerusalem, there are some mentions of "the dung gate." The English term translates a somewhat general Hebrew word which included garbage and trash. Obviously there was a particular gate, outside of which was located the city dump.

The bloodthirsty and repeated threat of the Old Testament is that which the King James Version renders as to cut off from a man's descendants every one "that pisseth against the wall." Whether the threat excluded boy babies, we need not argue. In any case, the situation seems to be that anything like a public urinal was as yet unknown and unneeded. Any wall served. Or, as in the often-repeated modern story, "Voilà, monsieur, toute la France!"

Besides its being beneath the dignity of most of the ancient writers, the chief reason that the disposal problem does not appear in literature is that it really was not yet important. Most cities were so small that the task of carrying debris out of the dung-gate and then dumping it was not arduous. Moreover, the amount of debris, per person, was ridiculously small by modern standards. Technology was simple, and society was far from affluent. Large numbers of people were poverty-stricken, and labor (often slave-labor) was cheap.

In a modern city, paper is one of the chief elements of waste; in an ancient city there was no paper at all. Glass is another modern problem, but in those times glass scarcely existed. Metal was much too valuable to be discarded, and even small bits were saved for scrap. Prunings and grass cuttings from both parks and private property supply many tons of material in a modern city, but the ancient city was tightly built, and generally parkless and treeless. Even yet, all around the Mediterranean, every bit of wood is treasured for the fire, and in ancient times, even straw, nutshells, and husks were probably burned.

What the slaves had to carry to the dung-gate, therefore, can be listed briefly—the cleanings of latrines, ashes in small quantities, some food-refuse such as bones and feathers, the occasional bodies of dogs and other unclean animals, now and then some broken tiles and pottery.

As yet there was no question of smog. Fire was still the all-cleansing element.

The tradition of the city, passing on from the Mediterranean lands toward modern America, reached northwestern Europe, without much change as far as the present subject-matter is concerned. The medieval city, and even Shakespeare's London, faced no new difficulties, and made, indeed, no advances.

An occasional passing reference in literature may be illuminating. The suggestion of Chaucer's *Miller's Tale* is that windows were freely used for human necessity. In his *Troilus and Criseyde*, Pandarus declares that he will support Troilus, even though he and his friends may lie like dead dogs in the street, words supplying evidence that no one worried much about the condition of the thoroughfares. If Falstaff was sitting by a "sea-coal fire," we may consider that the pall of bituminous-coal smoke was already beginning to hang over London.

The streets were narrow, with the gutter in the middle. The "slops" were thrown from the houses on both sides— sometimes with a cry or warning, sometimes without. The pedestrian walked along at his peril. The copious rains kept the streets somewhat cleared out, and swept the filth into the Thames, where no one worried any more about it, that water being brackish and not drinkable in any case.

Whether the disposal problem and the general sanitary conditions were better or worse in Elizabethan London than they were in Periclean Athens might be a matter for learned debate. Probably there was no great difference, and what there might be would result chiefly from differences in climate. Do you prefer dust (in Athens) to mud (in London)? Horses were commoner by the Thames than by the Aegean, but otherwise there is little change to note. Society was still not affluent, and there was not much that was thrown away. Paper had been invented, but it was expensive, and was saved for re-processing. Glass was scarce, and metal was still valuable for scrap. There were no slaves, but there was a large poverty-stricken group from which cheap labor could be drawn for unpleasant tasks.

London had its dumps. Even on the dumps "rakers" and "scavengers" earned a precarious living by sorting out what was still possibly edible, wearable, or salable. (Some highly respectable modern families apparently trace their names, such as Rakestraw, back to these "professional" origins.)

Elizabethan London was still roaring away when the English made their first attempts at colonization in America. Most of the colonists were ordinary Englishmen from the lower classes of society. They came from the filth and stench of London or from the agricultural villages, deep in manure. On the long voyage they had a chance to sniff the clean ocean air when they were on deck, but below deck the ship probably smelled worse even than London, what with crowding, lack of water, and seasickness.

The colonists approached what was still a clean and undefiled land, since the Indians were so few that they had made little impression. As something that we might treasure in our memories, as part of the long-time American dream, the first intimation that these colonists had of the new land was often the delicious fragrance that drifted out on the westerly breeze and could be recognized when the ship was miles from shore, even when there had been as yet no landfall. On July 2, 1584, Captain Arthur Barlowe reported:

We smelt so sweet, and so strong a smell, as if we had been in the midst of some delicate garden abounding with all kinds of odoriferous flowers, by which we were assured, that the land could not be far distant.

When they actually settled down to establish a colony, these Elizabethan Englishmen managed to make Jamestown, we should judge, no more cleanly than any other Elizabethan town, and the delicious fragrance vanished, soon overwhelmed by the smell of latrines, garbage, and not-often-washed bodies. The fevers and fluxes that almost exterminated the Jamestown colonists are usually credited to unsanitary conditions.

The Indians cannot be held to blame, and can hardly be held to have set a bad example. Their towns, as described by John Smith, were never large, not more than a few hundred people being gathered into one settlement. The houses were scattered, most of them standing alone in the midst of small fields or gardens.

Under such conditions, and with a simple culture, the question of disposal cannot have been acute. The inside of an Indian house may have been smelly and messy, but the villages as a whole gave a good impression to Captain Smith. The colonists could certainly have learned something from the Indians about such matters—but, of course, they did not. Essentially, they transported their own traditional customs to the New World. We cannot really blame them; men behave in that fashion.

Yet the land itself, especially its mere space, had an influence. Besides, there was no centuries-old accumulation of dirt to begin with. So, as far as we can tell, conditions in the English colonies, even when good-sized towns developed, never were as foul as they had been in London. Also, by the time of the growth of colonial towns, some higher standards of cleanliness were developing in England too.

One very important American change in the way of life had a great influence, and has passed its influence on, even to the present time. . . . The agricultural village was nearly universal in England, as well as on the continent. These villages approached being rural slums, where peasants lived with their animals, and went out every day to work in the fields. Any small settlement may be called a village, and there were plenty of these in the colonies. Most of them, however, were commercial and social, or rudimentarily industrial, with a store or two, a tavern, and perhaps a gristmill and a smithy. The farmers came in from round about to buy and sell, and to talk over a glass of ale, but they did not live in the village.

Instead, their homes were on individual family farms, and they were thus enabled to live, generally, under neater and more cleanly conditions than were prevalent in England or on the European continent. The group was small—two or three or four adults, and some children. Except for dogs and cats, the animals were kept at a distance, in the fields or in the barn and barnyard.

On the conception of such a farm was based Jeffersonian Democracy. It was, of course, an ideal, and the actual farm frequently failed to attain the ideal. Even a well-kept barnyard could become a horrible quagmire in bad weather. But, by and large, the American farm operated on a workable system. Though such farms are now comparatively rare, and may be on the way to becoming extinct, their psychological influence is still of importance, because so many still-vigorous people, as they say proudly, "were raised on a farm."

Of the many divisions of the disposal problem, as presented in the previous chapter, the people on a farm dodged most, and were not heavily afflicted by any. They had no sewers, and therefore no sewage. The old-fashioned privy—simple, efficient, and not necessarily unsanitary—served their needs. Garbage went to the hogs and chickens. Junk amounted to little more than a rusting harrow, a broken shovel, and some smashed crockery. There were no liquid effluents, unless a little soapy water could be so described. Manure was put on the fields. Some of it undoubtedly drained off into the streams, but not enough to do damage. Insecticides were unknown, though some people advocated throwing soapy water on rose bushes.

During most of the years of the flourishing of the farm, tin cans were unknown. Bottles were expensive and were treasured. Litter was no problem, and radioactivity had not even been invented.

Neither had the word *smog*. Smoke was merely smoke, and most of it was from clean oak and birch and hickory. Smoke went away, and no one knew where, or had to worry about it. Smoke was even aesthetic, with its plume of white or gray against the pale blue winter sky. Thoreau, that apostle of clean living, wrote several of his best poems on the loveliness of smoke and haze.

One of the famous literary presentations of the American farm is Whittier's *Snow-Bound*. Its picture is of a farm under very special conditions, but we should note that one of the chief chores, after the snowfall, was to shovel out a passageway to the barn. It was obviously at a commendable distance from the house; the Whittier family was not living in the smell of manure. . . .

As with the farm, so also the small town of a century ago presented no serious problem of disposal. Its people, too, had enough space.

Those townspeople used privies, set at a decent, though inconvenient, distance from the houses. Some unhonored practitioners, known by heavy-handed village humor as "honey-dippers," occasionally cleaned out the privies under cover of darkness. Now and then a typhoid epidemic swept the town, but most people had common sense enough, even if they lacked scientific knowledge, to dig their privies at a moderate distance from where they dug their wells.

Trash-burning and a town dump were universal. Hens (or even a pig) disposed of much of the kitchen waste, and a family dog might carry the bones away or even bury them.

The horses furnished the worst problem. Many families kept their own horse, or even a team, and draught-horses did all the work that trucks now do. Down until 1910 the streets of any town, generally unpaved, were thick with manure. . . .

When those people say, "I was raised on a farm," there is a tone of nostalgia in the voice, and even of surprise and wonder. Where, they seem to be saying, did that simplicity of life all vanish? Even in the cities, as older people can still remember them, there seems to have been little problem of disposal. Sewage went its way, and disappeared somewhere. Garbage was collected, and there is some memory that it was fed to hogs. But *now!* Why, within the lifetime of people still active—why has there been all the change, and for the worse?

Why these mountainous dumps, fouling both land and earth and air? Whence this green algae clogging the lakes? From what curse on the people have come these putrid streams? Even what was once the clean air itself—why does it now bring tears to the eyes?

3

GENESIS
OF A NIGHTMARE

HOWEVER SUBTLY the enormity of the disposal-problem may have encroached upon the United States, there is nothing mysterious or inexplicable about it. The development has occurred in about a century—let us say, from 1870. It may be attributed to four causes—increase of population, the growth of cities, the development of the "affluent" society, the invention of synthetic technology.

In 1870 the United States had fewer than forty million people; there are now five times as many. Other things being equal, five times as many people produce five times as much of a disposal problem. At the same time, however, the argument may run that five times as many people are available to care for the problem, so that it should be no worse.

There is, however, a fallacy in this argument. The people have increased, but the environment has not. Since 1870 only a few small areas, such as Hawaii, have been added. Merely because of growth of population, therefore, five times as much material must be dumped on the same land, or run into the same streams, or spewed into the same atmosphere. Moreover, the land has not improved its capacity for absorbing effluvia, nor have the streams grown more numerous or larger, nor has the atmosphere increased its size or speeded up its winds.

Merely because of more people, in the course of one century, the burden placed upon the environment has thus been multiplied approximately by five.

Even so, the fivefold increase in population is probably the least among the four reasons. Of much greater importance, certainly, is the concentration of people in cities.

In 1870 the census classified three-quarters of the persons in the United States as "rural." By definition, being rural meant that these people lived on farms or in villages or towns of fewer than 2,500 inhabitants. A hundred years later the situation has more than reversed itself. Only about one person in ten is rural, and nine out of ten are urban.

On an old-fashioned American farm, and in the small town, as the previous chapter has briefly indicated, people essentially took care of their own disposal problems. They did not find the labor excessive, and they did not, in the process and by their solution, either injure their own health appreciably or noticeably degrade their environment. Obviously they had the advantage that there was, so to speak, a lot of environment per person.

The modern city has gained a little by the elimination of most of the animals, though it still supports a flourishing and sometimes troublesome population of dogs and cats—to say nothing of such partially-domesticated and digestively active creatures as pigeons.

Except for fewer animals, the disposal problem of the city is many-fold worse than that of the farm or small town. The slice of environment available for each person is simply too thin. The amount of discarded material per acre goes up approximately in proportion to the number of people per acre. It may thus increase by a hundred or more. Even with the best of will (and the best of will is rare), the city-dweller has no way of disposing of his own waste. His dog has no place to bury a bone, and the very dog-droppings become a matter of city ordinance. The thought of a row of privies behind each apartment house is only humorous. The renter in the apartment house cannot burn his trash in the backyard, because there is no backyard. Even if there were, he could not burn the trash, because of fire hazard, smoke-and-smog regulations, and the necessities of his own nine-to-five day.

What happens is that the disposal of waste goes into the hands of specialists—all the way from garbage-men and street-cleaners to city engineers and smog-experts. The individual citizen pays, either through taxes or by special charge, to be relieved of the duty that he and his family would perform on the farm and even in the small town. The normal citizen pays unwillingly and with grumbles, and so he rarely pays enough.

As far as the urban individual is concerned, about all that he himself, or she herself, is willing to do is to put material into a garbage can. Even the idea that there should be more than one garbage can, for segregation of material, meets with general lack of cooperation. Hopefully, the individual uses the litter can on the street for the wrappings of a candy-bar and a pack of cigarettes, but the condition of the sidewalks suggests that even so much labor is resented. *Aren't there people who are paid to sweep things up, or can't the merchants have it done in front of their shops?*

The delegation of duties to paid workers is in harmony with the modern specilization of labor, and there is nothing wrong with it in theory. The trouble is that it costs money, and costs that money just to get rid of something that you have already used and had the fun out of. A species that still thinks, apparently, in terms of just dropping things out of the trees is not happy about thus spending money. Moreover, disposal by specialists can hardly begin until the original producer of the material has taken the first step.

Even worse, however, as far as the modern city is concerned, is the basically mathematical problem of the space-ratio. Land, water, and air simply cannot take the strain. In the more thickly inhabited regions, even now, city is beginning to merge with city, and the disposal problem pyramids. An isolated city still has a chance. Megalopolis is ready to founder under its load.

At the same time, let us remember, the city not only creates the problem but then also passes it on. Rivers that flow through a pleasant countryside may have been already polluted by the up-stream metropolis.

Schematically, to return to the idea of the conservation of matter, we may think of a city as a center into which civilization pours an appalling tonnage of material. Beneath the ground the unseen pipelines bring water, oil, and gas. On the ground, the all-too-visible railroads and highways contribute their endless freight trains and their innumerable trucks. By air, an ever-increasing load of freight arrives at the airports.

By the pipelines there is no outward movement at all, except insofar as sewers extend to disposal plants on the city's edge. By rail, road, and air, a comparatively small tonnage of manufactured goods is removed from the city, but most of this merely goes to some other city.

As anyone can see, this process tends to bury the city under the accumulation. The city, in the cheapest way possible, has been accustomed merely to dump its waste on the nearby ground, or into the streams and the air. The concentration of materials in cities, under the present system, is simply not being deconcentrated.

The third reason for the problem of what to do with things that you no longer want is what we generally mention with pride as "the affluent society." Our campaigns to end poverty mean that we are trying to extend affluence to people who do not have it already, and so we can only expect this phase of the problem of disposal to become correspondingly greater.

The affluent society is based partly upon the discovery that it is cheaper to produce something in quantity than to repair it. If the automobile part and its installation cost $6.24, and the mechanic's time to repair it would cost $7.14, obviously you are better off to get a new part. There is a slight fallacy, in that no one considers what happens to the old part. It is dumped somewhere, of course, and these thousands and thousands of discarded gadgets come to form a part of the engulfing mass.

This is only one of a thousand ways in which the affluent society increases the disposal problem—without, as a rule, doing anything about it. Americans have developed a psychological state of mind in which anything to do with saving or re-use is opprobrious. One of the few ethnic references still allowable is to call a person "Scotch." Or a person may be a "string-saver," or "chintzy," or a dozen things else. To utilize anything fully has become almost unpatriotic, since we are persuaded that the affluent economy depends upon rapid turnover.

We are psychologically adapted to throw things away readily—anything from a cigarette butt to the three-year-old car. We are equally careless about where we throw them.

Everyone, I suppose, likes affluence. Everyone, I suppose, approves of the affluent society.

In this connection, however, more clearly even than elsewhere, the central theme of this book is apparent. "You are not so rich as you think," because the American people are not taking care of the waste that they create, and it is catching up with them. Our civilization is going to have to come to a working agreement with the environment, or it is going to become such a disagreeable civilization as hardly to be worth living in—if, indeed, anyone can live in it at all. To come to some kind of balance with the environment is going to cost a great deal of money.

The situation appears strikingly if we again consider the

hundred-year perspective. Affluence was scarcely yet apparent in 1870. As an example, take paper, which is now the type and symbol of a thing of no value—"A mere scrap of paper!" ... "Not worth the paper it's written on!"

A hundred years ago paper was produced in comparatively small quantities, and was largely reprocessed, so that its disposal offered little problem. Occasionally, among old letters one comes upon a notable indication of the value of writing-paper, at least as late as the middle of the nineteenth century. In those times people sometimes filled the sheet in ordinary fashion, and then wrote across it again at right angles, thus getting twice as much writing on the page. It was a vile practice, and such letters are highly difficult to read. But it shows how valuable the paper was, in a society that had not yet grown affluent. That society continued to treasure such proverbs as "A penny saved is a penny earned!" and "Waste not, want not!"

In contrast, the current production of paper is between twenty-five and thirty million tons per annum. Only a small percentage of this remains intact even at the end of a year—stored up in libraries, or otherwise useful or potentially useful. About a third of the total is salvaged and goes into making new paper. The rest—fifteen million tons, to use a conservative figure—has been flushed down the sewers into the streams, or has added to the smoke problem, or has helped raise the dump heaps, or lies along the roadsides as litter.

The affluent society, as yet, cannot be bothered with the detail of waste paper, not even fifteen million tons of it a year.

Probably, the affluent society is more responsible for our troubles than is urbanization. Previous societies, even that of the United States a century ago, were not to be called affluent and at the same time they scarcely had a disposal problem. The same has been true of all the older societies, and it is still true of most of the world, where affluence has not yet raised its head.

Once I saw the contrast, with the sharpness of crossing a line. ... I was driving south through the Imperial Valley in California during the season of picking cotton. Along the highway the cotton-bolls lay, literally, as thick as snow. They had blown from the trucks that were taking the cotton from the fields to the gins. No one was making any effort to recover this cotton, though it was obviously as good as it ever was. Wages being what they were, the salvage of this escaped cotton simply did not pay. What became of this cotton? Probably it blew about, until it lodged against a fence or a rock, and eventually, after a winter or two and some rain, it went back into the soil. Doubtless it did no great harm, only producing an unaesthetic look in the countryside.

As we drove along, I made the obvious remark, "In any other country, someone would be out picking up this cotton."

An hour later we crossed into Mexico. There also the cotton lay by the road where it had blown from the trucks. But there the boys were walking along, each dragging a sack and picking up the cotton as he went.

The United States is affluent, and in many of the disturbing details of its current civilization it is paying the price of an easygoing affluence that has sprouted quickly, and has not yet learned to pick up behind itself.

A more subtle shift in modern civilization has been its synthesis and manufacture of useful and attractive materials that do not ordinarily exist in nature, and, once produced, are long-enduring or permanent within the human time-scale. They simply do not fit into any natural cycle of growth or decay.

Considered in terms of evolution, the situation becomes vivid. Throughout millions of years many creatures evolved with the specialty of what, from the human point of view, may be called "recycling." Termites reduced wood to powder. Many kinds of organisms, especially bacteria, served to expedite decay. Every process of nature thus had its counter-process.

But now some technologists produce a detergent or a plastic having a composition not known to nature. Unless we assume a conscious planning of the universe, we can hardly expect that through the ages some organism has been evolving with a digestive system adapted to the highly specialized new product—some organism, so to speak, that says, "Ha! This is just the food that I have been waiting for!"

The most widely publicized and the most spectacular of the new products are the atomic wastes. In one way we may consider it fortunate that the residues of fission are so deadly that they even become of international significance. Moreover, to date, their production has been limited to a few large operations. As a result, they hardly come into the ordinary problem of disposal, but are policed at a national level.

Much more involved with the ordinary person are such new synthetics as plastics, detergents, and insecticides. Commonplace and cheap, but long-lived and subtle, many such products linger on. They are not consumed by their use. They have been employed, and still are employed, without consideration of what becomes of them.

Scientists continue to discover new synthetics, and manufacturers continue enthusiastically to exploit them. A chemical company triumphantly proclaims in an advertisement that it will produce two hundred new products in a single year. The advertisement, however, gives no indication whether there has been any research as to how to get rid of these products after they have served their purpose.

Most of the new materials are produced in small quantities, and are inert, after use. Others, inevitably, create trouble.

The problem of what to do with the discarded synthetics is quantitatively a small one, but the resistance to decay and the virulence of some of the materials raise serious threats, and the possible long-range difficulties threaten the health of the human race and the beneficence of the environment. . . .

Thus arising, the whole situation of disposal seems so closely involved with civilization itself as to be automatically produced and essentially insolvable. The crisis appears to be desperate, and it may well be so.

There is even the possibility that civilization has already passed some point of no return. No one, indeed, knows what the effect upon the race may have been from the release of radioactive materials, and what the effect upon the environment may be from the accumulation of pesticides, carbon dioxide, and the constituents of smog.

No one knows, moreover, how great may have been the psychological effects upon the millions of individuals who constitute society. A majority of them may have become used to a regime of dirt and confusion, so that they merely consider it a normal way of life.

Even if the problem is considered to be basically nothing more than economic, it may be such a large one as to pass the limits of self-discipline which the present generation is willing to impose upon itself. We may flinch from the charges, and prefer to let those charges be absorbed by the cumulative degradation of the environment.

There are also, however, some reasons for optimism and hope. What man has done, that also, one would think, man can undo. At least, before surrendering we should look at the situation in more detail.

The optimist, moreover, need not be wholly beaten down. He may still quote, "The other side of a problem is an opportunity." Inherent in certain phases of the complicated processes of disposal—notably, in connection with sewage—are revolutionary new processes for the maintenance of civilization.

4

SEWAGE

The fundamental problem

As THE MILLENNIA have passed, rivers have always been closely entwined with the life of man. The flowing stream quenched the thirst both of man and of his flocks and herds; it supplied him with fish and frogs and waterfowl; it offered recreation, as the children splashed in the sunny shallow and the strong man dived into the clear pool.

The involvement of man and rivers was not altogether beneficent. Some streams harbored the terror of the crocodile. The river-god was always chancy, and might seize a swimmer by the heels and pull him under, or even sweep the whole village with a flood.

Yet, generally, man loved the river, and it even worked into his proverbs: "Still waters run deep," ... "Follow the river, and you come to the sea." So also, the river became part of his poetry: "the river of life," ... "All the rivers run into the sea," ... "Even the weariest river," ...

"Where Alph the sacred river ran," ... "By shallow rivers, to whose falls. ..."

All the poetry and beauty of a river, however, cannot blind any thinking man to the reality that rivers are, after all, the continent's natural sewers. Much that originates on land, in solution or as sediment, drains down into the streams until it reaches in the end that cosmic sink, the ocean itself.

In earlier times even a deep-thinking man did not need to be disturbed about the situation. The river could carry its natural load, and men were so few and so scattered that pollution by human means seemed, and probably was, unimportant. There was even a saying, "Running water purifies itself," a dangerous half-truth.

Then, in our own times, came the shocking alteration. At sunset, from a distance, the river was still as beautiful as ever. But everyone knew the truth—that the river had now become, and no longer in a merely figurative sense, a sewer. At low water it even stank. The fish, even the frogs, had vanished; the waterfowl had little reason to alight. Stooping to drink at the stream's edge was unthinkable. Even to swim was dangerous and stomach-turning. One of man's most ancient partners had at last been, as it were, betrayed, and was now fouled and horrible. ...

Sewage, which has chiefly worked the degradation of the waters, is of itself highly complicated. Its origin is basically duplex.

It consists, first, of the so-called "sanitary sewage," which most people would consider to be sewage par excellence, if the expression may be allowed in such connection. Moreover, it traditionally presents the fundamental problem of disposal. The essential constituents of this part of the whole sewage are the excreta of human beings. This means, in an urban community, the flushings of toilets.

Sanitary sewage is both offensive and dangerous, the latter because it carries a heavy load of bacteria, which may be disease-producing.

Mingled with the flushings is all the drainage of washbasins, baths, and kitchen-sinks, greatly increased in recent years by the output of garbage-disposal units, and with the added load of detergents and other non-degradable synthetics.

The second element of sewage consists of what may be called "natural drainage," that is, rainwater and melted snow. This water washes off the streets and buildings, and so picks up a miscellaneous collection of dirt and impurities—scattered paper; the droppings of dogs, rats, and pigeons; oil and grease; soil from construction work; anything else that can be dissolved, floated off, or washed away.

The inclusion in the same pipes of so much that is different both in quality and in origin has led to constant, repeated, and sometimes successful attempts to keep separate the two components of sewage, and to pass them through different channels to different disposals. Theoretically, the separation appeals to everyone—sanitary drains for household effluents, and storm drains for rainwater. As it is, a storm often brings such a deluge that the existing sewers are unable to handle the load. They overflow, spewing out sanitary sewage along with the surface run-off. Citizens of some of our metropolises, too inured to the sight to be much shocked, feast their eyes upon the sight of toilet paper floating along the gutters.

"Combined" suggests something that, having been separate, has been brought together. Historically, such a conception cannot be justified for sewers. They began as ditches which were dug or enlarged to drain swamps and to convey rainfall into the rivers. Where these ditches ran through towns, the townspeople soon came to find them handy for the disposal (though this was never a real or final disposal) of all sorts of filth and unwanted odds and ends. Such, in Shakespeare's London, was the famous Fleetditch, and such also was Moorditch which even Falstaff (not a man of great delicacy) considered "most unsavory." Eventually the ditches became so noisome that they were arched over. They still carried rainwater, and people still dumped their refuse in through inlets. Finally, when houses were supplied with outlet pipes, these pipes flowed into the same old ditch, which by this time might be called a "combined" sewer.

No sanitary engineer or tax-expert has as yet solved the problem of separation. Many sewers still carry the materials from the storm-water and household effluents, and there is even much good argument that they should. Street scourings are about as dirty as the other materials, and so are not particularly degraded by being mixed with them. What we need is a system, of the one kind or the other, large enough and well enough designed to get the work to be done. That, unfortunately, is cities of even the wealthy United States do not possess. With greater concentration of people and rising affluence, most sewage-systems are becoming more inadequate year by year. More toilet paper, rather than less, is likely to be floating in the gutters. Many parts of the country are already at the edge of a crisis. . . .

As with so much in civilization, even such a materialistic problem as the disposal of sewage is tied up closely with human thoughts and feelings. Especially, with regard to the sanitary fraction, any program of disposal must face what amounts to a kind of prejudice, springing from the various attitudes of man as he has developed out of savagery.

In the beginning man's excreta were only another kind of dirt, of some inconvenience. Later, they developed a touch of magic, since they seemed to be a part of man's body that had separated itself, but might still have an effect. Our most basic four-letter noun, in fact, is cognate with the Latin *scindere,* and means something separated.

Another stage arose with the realization, among agricultural peoples, that the material was a valuable fertilizer. The Orientals, especially the Chinese, thus recycled the excreta by carefully returning them to the fields. Western peoples typically kept more domestic animals and used the manure, though they often mingled their own excreta with it. . . .

A third attitude could arise only in the later nineteenth century, with the discovery of pathogenic bacteria, and the indubitable role of sewage in such ravaging plagues as typhoid and cholera. What had previously been suspected, now was surely known. Sewage, which had been not worse than distasteful and might even be considered valuable, with new knowledge was classified as dangerous. The maintenance of "safe" supplies of water became a primary duty of government, and the sanitary engineer and the public-health officer tended to become dictators—though with minds directed toward "health" in the narrower sense, and with generally little interest in the maintenance of a beautiful or happiness-oriented environment.

Finally, present for a long time but especially developed with the twentieth century, has been the idea of obscenity and the establishment of a taboo with sexual connotations. 0 young couples went out courting behind some and they learned, literally, to face the chance for conversation in the Tradition, indeed, indicates that a visit to the garderobe was an occasion of sociability. Largely because of the growing affluence, which allows the privacy of many "bathrooms," the excretory process became more and more cloaked in secrecy. To walk in a park or across a campus, these days, impresses anyone that sex, just short of the climactic act, has moved into the open daylight. But elimination is more under taboo than ever before. Such a situation is not without its larger implications. The suggestion of the use of human fertilizer, for instance, raises shrieks which apparently do not spring so much from largely fanciful sanitary hazards as from suggestions of obscenity and indecency. . . .

The whole modern problem of sewage is twofold—first, to collect it; second, to dispose of it in the stricter sense.

The collection by means of pipelines is so much a part of our tradition and our way of living that we can scarcely imagine anything else, and we do not stop to consider its fantastic elaboration and its monstrous inefficiency. How many times has each of us seen the street torn up, and tax-money in the thousands expended upon repairing or replacing a few pipes!

Each of our cities sits upon a mare's nest of thousands of miles of small and large conduits displaying a vague dendritic structure, through which foul water runs and from which foul odors arise, the latter to be kept from entering our houses only by what seems the frail intervention of countless water-traps. The disposal-pipes are fed by millions—literally, millions—of small inlets. The sewage-system of a city is in fact so fantastic as to deserve some such rarely-used adjective as chimerical. It provides a good example of something that started—in this case, two or three centuries ago—in a simple, reasonable, and cheap way, by the gradual adaptation of the natural drainage. Once a start had thus been made, the line of least resistance always was, not to scrap the already-made investment, but to go ahead to greater and greater elaboration.

Anyone starting out from scratch to plan a civilization would hardly have designed such a monster as our collective sewage system. Its existence gives additional point to the sometimes asked question, "Is there any evidence of intelligent life on the planet Earth?"

As what might, for instance, be called a minor detail, all sewer-systems leak. Considering their many miles of pipes, we can never expect perfection. Errors in manufacture of pipes and errors in installation, movement of earth, action of roots—all work to produce leaks. Then, in wet weather, rainwater drains into the sewers, and in dry weather sewage goes out into the soil. And we can never expect anything else.

Besides, in the United States, most of the systems were planned and basically constructed in the nineteenth century, when cities were much smaller, and when affluence had not yet established the joyousness of being wasteful. In those days, for instance, many housewives normally saved water by not flushing the toilet after every use.

The really amazing fact is that our elaborately-piped systems of sewage-collection still manage to work at all. Expensive, leaky, always falling into disrepair, haunted with the threat of future inadequacy—yet they function from day to day. The city-dweller still presses the lever with high confidence that the thing will work and at least pass the problem on to the next stage, without either blowing up in his face or just going gurgle.

The basic inefficiency, however, is enough to make both angels and experts weep. The daily excreta of a healthy human being, expressed as dry solid, amount to about half a pound. Yet, the flushing of these ounces down the pipes requires the expenditure of many pounds of water.

Ordinary sewage is thus estimated to contain only one-tenth of 1 per cent of solid material. We might then maintain that it consists of 99.9 per cent pure water.

An ideal solution would be to separate the 0.1 per cent of solids, and then run the pure water off into the streams. The solid material, though still considerable, would be of small enough bulk and weight to be economically transportable.

Instead, at one stage of the process, the estimate is that we use 2000 tons of water to move *one* ton of solid. The inefficiency is appalling. As one critic has put it, "A dozen good burros could do better."

But the solution can be determined more precisely than in terms of burros. By the figures already stated, a city of a million people produces as daily excreta, the essential matter of sewage, a half-million pounds of dry solid, that is, only 250 tons. The removal of such an amount of material would be child's play for the leviathans of modern transportation. Ironically, not the material itself, but the water used as carrier, has come to be the problem.

Another approach would be to increase the load of solids, since the carrying power of flowing water is much higher than most sewage is at present required to maintain. Some experts therefore support the use of garbage-disposal units as a way of utilizing the already functioning sewage pipe more efficiently. In this way the already existing set of pipes might further aid in the outflow of materials from the more and more overburdened urban areas. On the other hand, the disposal-problem would thus be further complicated.

So fixed, indeed, is the tradition of water-borne sewage in our civilization and even in our personal feeling that the very imagination flinches before any other idea. Yet one should not forget the earth-closet, as invented, developed, and promulgated around 1860 by the Reverend Henry Moule, of Fordington Vicarage, Dorsetshire, England. Since he was thus a functioning officer of the Church of England, we must assume that Mr. Moule was at least indifferently honest and more or less in his right mind. According to him and to his many disciples in the later nineteenth century, the earth-closet was efficient, wholly inoffensive to have in the house, cheap, simple to work. At least one American company manufactured and distributed it.

From a hopper filled with earth, the pulling of a lever or even the rising of the person from the seat, sifted some dry earth into the bowl. All odor was thus contained, and the excreta rapidly decomposed and mingled with the earth. They mingled indeed so well that the result could eventually be used again, though this petty economy need not be obligatory.

But note the efficiency in the minimal bulk of product. According to Mr. Moule's published figures, one person needed only *two pounds of earth a day*. This figure, moreover, was based upon the necessarily crude engineering of a nineteenth-century country parson. What could not our modern experts have developed along this line?

Though the earth-closet may now be considered as visionary as Lost Atlantis, a sanitary engineer may be permitted to view its memory with a secret yearning. It would certainly have solved some problems. We can imagine the few pounds of earth being picked up like garbage, or even in a proper container being picked up with the garbage. Vanished, indeed, would be the flush-toilet, and an army of plumbers would have to be otherwise employed. Gone, also, would be a multitude of public-health problems, though we might, indeed, have some new ones.

...

Yet, fantastic though it may be, our apparatus for the collection of sewage continues to work, after a fashion. When we come to the final disposal of sewage, this is different. It has never worked very well, and now it is definitely ceasing to work.

The original system was to collect the sewage into larger and larger conduits, and then to allow these conduits to empty into the natural drainage. As cities grew, the originally limpid woodland streams and the outflows of the crystal springs became—first undrinkable, then unsmellable, finally, unspeakable and unthinkable. Such former streams, covered over, form the main sewers under most American cities. From these sewers the great volume of polluted water—sometimes intercepted temporarily in disposal plants, sometimes not—eventually passes into the still-flowing streams.

The question has been raised as to whether the present system works. One reply might be similar to that of Bernard Shaw when asked whether Christianity worked. He said that it had never been tried. So also, the United States has probably never had a large-city disposal system that was adequately designed, large enough, and up-to-date. But whether it fails to work because it is basically wrong or because it has not been properly installed makes rather little difference.

Some might even claim that the present system works, and we might therefore examine it a little. . . . Of 190 million people, a third of them still have no sewers at all. Very vague figures indicate that as many as half of this group, nearly all of them in the rural areas, depend upon the old-fashioned privy—inconvenient, unsightly, status-destroying, but not necessarily unsanitary, and possessing a pleasant social and intimate suggestion, of which James Whitcomb Riley and Chic Sale have made much.

The badly constructed and improperly located privy can be a menace. Drainage from it contaminates the surface water and the ground water. It attracts insects and other carriers of disease. It smells. Still, in the modern world, the privy as an institution is far off, surrounded by plenty of space, a vestigial problem from the past.

More than 30 million other sewerless people are served by septic tanks. Most of these people live in modern suburban areas, and the status of the septic tank is high. So is its sanitary functioning, until it breaks down—as, it is calculated, one in three does within three years. On the whole, however, the tank may be, in the long run, an expense and a nuisance to its owner, but it is generally situated in areas of low concentration of people, and so it does not greatly complicate the problem of disposal.

The difficulties really arise with the 125 million people who contribute to the sewers. Of these, more than 12 million are attached to pipelines that merely discharge "raw" sewage into streams. In addition, over 30 million people live in communities that thus release the material after only "primary" (read, inadequate) treatment. Even the more enlightened communities are forced to bypass much sewage in a raw condition during times of heavy rainfall. The conclusion of the expert is, "Sewage discharges correspond to the raw sewage from almost 50 million people."

As a whole, with such figures, the system can scarcely be said to be working successfully. Water-borne diseases, indeed, are no longer a day-to-day threat. This desirable consummation has been effected, however, not so much by cleaning up the sewage as by taking the dirty water, and then treating it by filtration and chlorinization so that it is biologically harmless, if not exactly aesthetic. Like the village where people lived by taking in each other's laundry, much of the United States lives by drinking the water that has already been used for sewage by some upstream city. The situation is the worse because the nation is continental, and many of the cities are strung like beads on the string of some long river—especially the Mississippi and its great tributaries, the Ohio and the Missouri.

The water tastes a little of chlorine-compounds, and the thought of what you are drinking may be repulsive, but these may be considered small prices to pay for civilization. You will not contract typhoid or cholera, and the rather narrow objectives of public health have been attained. Biologically the water is "pure." Thus far, the system is working.

There is, indeed, an occasional breakdown, as when 18,000 people in Riverside, California, went down with gastroenteritis (and a few of them died) from *Salmonella typhimurium* in the drinking water. Such incidents are disturbing, especially if you live in Riverside. Anything of the sort raises the unpleasant suggestion that the system is not working quite so well as we usually assume, and that it may be heading for more trouble as population increases.

But there is also something more. . . . Let us suppose
and grant a perfect germicidal solution. We must still face
the basic problem of conservation of matter. The 99.9 per
cent of water creates no great difficulty. But what of the
0.1 per cent of solid? Even such a small fraction runs into
thousands of tons for a large city in the course of a year.
What is it, and what become of it?

By the natural processes of life much of this tonnage
combines with the oxygen that is already dissolved in the
water and then passes off into the atmosphere as carbon
dioxide. This omnipresent gas is inert, invisible, tasteless,
and odorless, and in the more immediate human terms is
harmless. (What it may do in the atmosphere, in the long
run, has to be considered later.)

In addition, the decomposition of sewage results chiefly
in nitrates and phosphates. These compounds are basic
fertilizers, and their addition to a stream or lake might be
thought excellent for the stimulation of plant growth and
eventually of fish and other aquatic life. So it is, if the
concentration is low. But, as anyone who has even tried to
raise a potted geranium may be expected to know, too
much fertilizer is deadly.

It is all a question of degree. Lakes generally seem to
suffer more than rivers from overfertilization. Since the
water of a good-sized lake requires years for a full
change, the fertilizing compounds gradually increase their
concentration. Species after species of aquatic life, plant
and animal, suffers a crossing of its threshold of existence,
fails to reproduce, and dies out. The dominant growth to
remain is the green algae. Lake Erie has largely suc-
cumbed, along with dozens or hundreds of smaller bodies
of water. Already threatened is the famous alpine beauty
of Lake Tahoe.

In another way also, especially in streams and estuaries,
the dumping of sewage works havoc. The natural process
of decay which yields carbon dioxide demands oxygen.
This oxygen has to come from that which is dissolved in
the water, and the amount that can thus be dissolved is
strictly limited. Once used, it can be restored by absorp-
tion from the air, but the replenishment is slow, especially
for a deep and slow-moving stream.

In primitive times the whole process was a natural and
healthful one for the stream. The concentration of animals
and men in the watershed was low, and much of the

material that is now hastily run off as sewage then rested on the land and returned to the soil for the renewal of fertility. With civilization, in many watersheds, man has simply become too numerous. The streams have become overloaded. When demand for oxygen grows too great, the amount of dissolved oxygen begins to decline. As when overfertilization occurs, species after species dies out. The game fish are early to perish; the trash fish remain a while longer. After a while, even the bottom growth begins to fail. Eventually the oxygen content approaches zero.

Most people, in the course of education, have seen the experiment in which a candle is set to burn in a closed space. When the oxygen is exhausted, the flame dies. So it is in the stream. With the disappearance of that essential element, the light of life winks out. All that can remain are a few of those lower forms of plants which are known as anaerobic, that is, capable of living without free oxygen, and which produce, or are associated with, repulsive conditions and foul smells.

Again, the unescapable law of conservation of matter has taken charge. We can transform sewage, but we cannot destroy it. Somewhere its constituents must remain, and in actual practice they most noticeably remain in the lakes and streams. We of civilization have ruined our waters by befouling them, or are rapidly so doing, because we are merely dumping the materials of our sewage in the easiest way, that is, in the cheapest way.

We must do better. We must, first of all, restore the situation. Second, we must continue to keep it decent. We are in the situation of someone discovering that he has heavy unpaid bills of which he was ignorant, and also that he will continue to have heavier bills in the future. *Not so rich as you think!* ...

In one way the solution may be said to be obvious. Since we cannot get rid of the stuff, we must do something else with it. We can put it where it is at least doing no harm—as in any primitive but well-placed and well-constructed privy. Or we can put it to some good use. The latter solution really means to recycle the now useless or harmful material so that it again becomes, not a hindrance, but an aid to life.

Since nitrates and phosphates are valuable fertilizing materials, the natural step would seem to be to return them to the land. This procedure has to combat, first of all, an almost religious fixation against the use of human fertilizer. It involves, second, a strenuous objection from the fertilizer companies, reinforced by a good many agricultural experts, or "experts." The argument would run that the fertilizer value of sewage per gallon or per ton is so low that the process of returning it to the land would be uneconomic. Cheaper, the argument can run, to fix the atmospheric nitrogen and to dig concentrated phosphate from the earth, than to process, transport, and distribute the sewage! But the fallacy of this argument is that something has to be done with the sewage in any case, if life in much of our country is to remain worth living. Economically, in the larger view, we might be better off even if we had to pay the farmer for allowing us to dump the sewage on his land.

The solution by way of fertilizer offers two basic possibilities ... First, the sewage can be treated and concentrated near the city, and the great bulk of it then run off into the streams as pure water, or pure-enough water. The concentrated sludge then exists in large tonnages, but not too large for handling by established methods of transport by rail and road, or by barge and freighter. Unfortunately, the sludge is itself of limited value as a fertilizer, cannot compete with the commercial product, and is, in fact, not really worth transporting and spreading on the fields. One experimental attempt has been to enrich the sludge with commercial fertilizer, but the efforts of the city of Milwaukee have scarcely met with economic success. In any case, however, the processing itself is expensive and the transportation is more so. The experts and the salesmen for the fertilizer companies seem to have a case in maintaining that the procedure is not "economic." We may agree, if we interpret "economic" simply in the sense of making a profit. It may, however, be advantageous, if the necessity of getting rid of the sewage is figured into the bookkeeping.

The second possibility is to transport the liquid sewage without treatment. The tonnage thus to be moved is tremendous and appalling. Yet, we must remember, all this matter has, in some way, been transported into the cities. If civilization can bring it in, civilization should also be able to take it out. Moreover, transportation of a liquid by pipeline is one of the cheapest means. Large pipelines and many tank-trucks would be required, and the charges for pumping would always be considerable. But there would be some economies over the present system in that much or all of the treatment of sewage could be omitted. Moreover, the distances involved would not be great. Thousand-mile pipelines now transport oil. Under present American conditions, sewage would probably not have to be transported more than fifty miles. Even so, the procedure might not be practical.

Another possibility is more imaginative and more radical—in fact, fantastically revolutionary in human history. Since the Neolithic period, agriculture has been basic to human existence. Men, in country and city alike, have depended upon the food laboriously, and often precariously, won from the cultivation of the fields. Now, for the first time, arises the possibility that the agricultural process may be bypassed, and basic food be produced by what can be called a factory method.

Easily cultured in a retaining pool, under sunlight, certain kinds of algae multiply with great rapidity in ordinary effluent. With the aid of bacteria, in an amazingly short time, they "consume" the sewage, that is, they transform the sewage into algae.

Moreover, these algae in themselves are highly nutritious, like grass or hay, for certain types of digestive systems. Separated out, they become food for poultry or cattle. By laboratory methods they can easily be concentrated and dried, but at a mass level the process is difficult, and to the present time has been economically doubtful. Almost certainly new ideas will be worked out, and one of these is already being put forward.

To appreciate what may happen we should again consider the background. . . . American civilization, as we may put it, envisages a linear and one-way disposal by which sewage is conceived as eventually reaching the ocean, and thus disappearing, unutilized. The scheme may be shown graphically:

Crops ⟶ Food ⟶ Sewage ⟶ Stream ⟶ Ocean

By such a process the fertility of the land constantly drains off into the ocean. Many nineteenth-century prophets of gloom saw in this system the eventual advance of sterility and the ruin of Western civilization. Twentieth-century philosophers have not been so much concerned, perhaps because progress has furnished them with so many other ways in which Western civilization can ruin itself more quickly.

In contrast, some civilizations, such as that of China, have conceived the whole life process as circular. Men ate the crops, from them produced their own excreta, returned these to the fields as fertilizers, and thus produced new crops. The loss or wastage was minimal. This scheme can be represented:

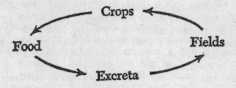

The highly complicated (and, therefore, weak) point in this system is that which is here labeled, with deceptive simplicity, "Fields." All the toils and risks of agriculture are here involved—fertilizing, tilling, planting, cultivation, protection, harvesting, processing. Moreover, at this stage the whole cycle is at the mercy of nature, and the transition from *Fields* to *Crops* may be broken by drought, flood, blight, locusts, frost, and a myriad of other disasters. Only with periodic famine to set the balance right can the system function.

With a new conception of the factory transformation of sewage, a new scheme can be set up, also a circular one.

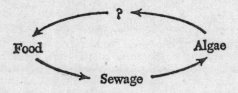

As shown by the question mark, the process is not yet complete, but there are ideas, and there have been experiments. Chicken feed is actually being produced from algae.

One possibility is to introduce, in another step, some organism that feeds naturally on algae—such as the daphnia, or so-called water flea. This creature has a voracious appetite, and feeds on algae as sheep on clover. Remembering the conservation of mass, and neglecting what passes off as gas, we may conceive a ton of sewage becoming a ton of algae and then a ton of algae passing on to be a ton of water fleas. Water fleas are large enough to be strained out, thus leaving behind water which is pure enough even for drinking without chlorinization. The water can then be run into the streams without degrading them, and the water fleas can be passed on for further treatment.

They are high in protein. Chemical processing can separate from them their oils and other unpleasant materials, thus leaving still a certain residue, though one of small enough proportions not to raise too difficult a disposal problem. The purified material now bears no closer relationship to water fleas than wheat flour does to soil and manure. It can be considered a basic food. Probably it will not be tasteful, but merely insipid. So is wheat flour. Yet from flour as a base the chef concocts some very tasty morsels.

The usual reaction of most people at this point is to say, "Water fleas! Well, I prefer to eat beefsteak."

There are two possible replies: "Very well," one answer can be, "that is a typical retort of affluence. But even now two-thirds of the people in the world are said to go to bed hungry. At the present rate of population growth, in fifty years (and you may still be alive then) the population of the United States will be so dense that you will eat food prepared from water-flea flour, and like it." (Of course, it will not by that time be called "water-flea flour." Madison Avenue, or its successor, will have coined some attractive and succulent-sounding term.)

The other answer is, "Probably you actually will—in the beginning, at least—eat your water fleas in the form of beefsteak, after the meal made from them has been utilized as cattle fodder. Or, you may eat them in the form of omelets, sausage, roast turkey, or lamb chops, after the sources of those dainties have been fed on the meal."

In spite of various hazards, some such development is likely to occur. In the first place, it will help to solve the critical problem of sewage disposal. In the second place, it will largely bypass agriculture, and thus permit the use for recreation and general living of much space now pre-empted by crops and pastureland—and this at a time when man in all the civilized parts of the world is beginning to press upon his limits of openness. To be sure, a slight increase in the birthrate will fill the space again in a generation, but there will be at least a pleasant interval. Civilized man may have another chance. Ladies and gentlemen, this may be the biggest thing since the invention of the wheel. . . .

The problem of sewage is ancient, but it is also contemporary, and pressing. The United States is still committed to nineteenth-century methods, to a physical setup of aging pipes, and to certain archaic modes of thought. All of these may be considered obsolescent.

Merely to modernize the equipment for the collection of sewage, without consideration of treatment and disposal, is estimated to require an expenditure of twenty billion dollars. If one insists upon the nicety of separating sanitary sewage from mere run-off, that will be, please, twenty billion more. And, still beyond that, lies the question of disposal.

At the same time, "the other side of a problem is an opportunity." As the suggestion has here been offered, there is no greater opportunity in the world today than arises in connection with the lowly matter of the recycling of sewage. Hope may exist still that man's old love for the waters of the earth may be renewed, that the lakes again show blue in the sunshine, that the rivers run undefiled.

5

FACTORY EFFLUENTS

Affluence vs. effluence

CURRENT AMONG disposal buffs, is a saying, "Instead of the Affluent Society ours should be known as the Effluent Society."

From the Latin *ex fluere*, the term should include everything that "out-flows," that is, all water-borne waste. In common practice the usage is confined to what are, more specifically, "factory effluents," those horrifying conglomerations—ill-smelling, nauseously-colored, fish-smothering, and even poisonous—that flow from factories into streams and lakes. About the only disagreeable material that this discharge does *not* theoretically contain is ordinary sewage, although some of that slips in also. In any case, though different in origin and composition, sewage and factory effluents are alike in being chiefly deleterious as water-pollutants, and they cannot, therefore, be wholly separated in presentation.

Since factories themselves are relatively new, dating only from the Industrial Revolution of the later eighteenth century, factory effluents are also new. There are a few exceptions. Slaughterhouses, at least for several centuries, have caused trouble for downstream residents by dumping blood and offal into the helpless river. Tanneries also have been traditional offenders.

Such industries, especially because of the stench that they raised, came to be known as the "unpleasant trades," and the workmen thus involved had to suffer from the disdain of more lucky laborers and were often shunned—understandably, in view (though this is hardly the word) of the more-than-body odor that emanated from them. In this connection, one should recall that workers with the

45

bodies of dead animals are among the Untouchables in India.

From 1800 on, factories multiplied in number, grew in size, and correspondingly increased their output, including their output of refuse, most of it in liquid form. Not all factories thus contributed, but a large proportion of them did so, especially those involved with heavy tonnages of basic natural materials, such as iron, paper, and sugar. Certain other industries added, not so much bulk, but rather a concentrate of unpleasantnesses, many of them poisonous, as with dyeworks, chemical plants, and metal-plating works. Even some seemingly beneficent processes were far from blameless, if we for the moment assume the point of view of a fish. "Dairy products" might have an innocent sound, but there is a surprising amount of whey to be dumped. Packing plants have to wash their fruits and vegetables, and then return the dirty, pesticide-laden water to the stream.

This pollution was, if not justified, at least permitted, under the riparian laws of England. In the seventeenth century, there being as yet no reason to raise questions, this code was transferred to the American colonies. The law, in particular, was concerned with the *quantity* of water. A landowner could not bypass the flow so as to deprive his downstream neighbor, for instance, of a sufficient head of water to operate his mill wheel. But ashes and manure could be dumped into the stream. The problem of pollution had simply not become acute enough for the law to take notice—*De minimis non curat lex*. On the contrary, recent legislation has been forced to be much concerned with the *quality* of water. . . .

The end result in the twentieth century, to state it bluntly, has been the befouling of the larger streams across the continent. A published list of such ruined rivers includes examples from every one of the contiguous states. Rhode Island is not too small. Wyoming is not too high-set and isolated.

Included in the list are the streams that have been household words for centuries, woven into the texture of American history—the Hudson, Susquehanna, Potomac, Connecticut, French Broad, Yadkin, Savannah, Big Horn. Washington crossing the Delaware today would be realistically painted in no more heroic posture than holding his nose. In the list of lifeless rivers are those celebrated in poetry and song—the Suwannee, Wabash, Chattahoochee.

Here also are the Mississippi with its chief tributaries—
Mark Twain's river now being sometimes known as "the
colon of the Middle West." Another polluted stream is the
Columbia, which in its very name stands as a symbol of
the whole nation. A saint's name is no guarantee of
purity, and the St. Francis and the St. Joseph flow equally
dirty. So also polluted are streams with names that still
seem to suggest canoes and war bonnets more than stench
—the Animas, Apalachicola, Menominee, Marais des
Cygnes, Palouse, Big Sioux, Muskingum, Nishnabotna.
The Merrimack, a little befouled even when Thoreau
spent his week there in 1839, has now drawn the epithet
"obscene." Also on the list, far off on the plains, are
streams that the covered wagons followed—the Big Blue,
the Little Blue, both branches of the Platte.

As far as major streams are concerned, one can more
economically check off those that are not on the list—not
yet, at least, heavily polluted. Among the few to be thus
distinguished would be the Sacramento, Cumberland, and
Humboldt.

The best that can be said is that the headwaters of the
streams maintain some degree of purity. Trout still rise in
the feeders of the Yellowstone, though oil refineries have
done their devastation farther down.

There is even a kind of perverse competition for dirtiest
of all our rivers—a Miss America of Pollution. Senator
Edmund S. Muskie of Maine, a leader in the struggle for
pure water, nominates his own Androscoggin, rich with
the redolence of paper mills. But the Mahoning of Pennsylvania and Ohio is a good contender, by virtue of the
steel-mills. Recently the newsmen of Detroit, realizing that
their own rivers were high on the list, nominated Cleveland's little Cuyahoga as having attained the acme of
lifeless befoulment.

Lakes also are affected, along with estuaries and even
shallow bays. The tidal waters of Long Island and New
Jersey have received special study, and are known to be
badly polluted. Man may not yet have been able to encroach seriously upon the oceans, but he is already working in around the edges. And, unfortunately, these edges
are the part of the oceans most intimately associated with
the life of man.

As yet, however, rivers are the most common sufferers
from effluents ... Always, we may say, an affinity has
existed between factories and rivers. Some manufacturers

were seeking water power and water transportation; others were seeking water to use in the complex and manifold new processes that were developing. Again, however, as with the list of rivers, one could probably list more easily those manufacturing processes which did not need water than those that did. "Those that were offenders," some might say. But we should be careful with such words. These manufacturers in large degree created modern civilization. If they were careless with how they disposed of their residues, they were only behaving like other people, in the old tradition of the arboreal animal. In the long run, as often happens, public opinion changed, and even law along with it. In the later twentieth century, certainly, many manufacturers can be properly called "offenders" against the public interest and even against the law.

The amount of water taken into factories—and then, what is really to the point, run out again into the streams—is so great as to be essentially beyond comprehension for the ordinary person in any common units. One can only say that it consists of whole rivers-full.

The amount needed per unit of product may be interesting and curious, but again it means little to the ordinary person. Fifteen gallons of water are required for one of beer, and eighty of water for one of whiskey. The river must supply 150 tons of water to allow the factory to produce one ton of paper. One ton of aluminum demands about a thousand tons of water.

The total amount of water is naturally dependent upon the total tonnage of output. Acetic acid, though it is per unit a heavy user, is itself produced in such small tonnages as to be comparatively unimportant. Gasoline is just the opposite—having a low requirement per unit, but a tremendous tonnage. Other heavy users, in gross, are beet sugar, paper, textiles, and steel.

The law of the conservation of matter being what it is, factories do not "use" water in the sense of consuming or destroying it. They do not, except in minute degree, break it down into its elements, hydrogen and oxygen. Even the comparatively small fraction that they vaporize is not lost. Steam that mounts into the air from a factory chimney in Chicago will return as rain or snow or dew somewhere, perhaps on the fields of Ohio. If factories actually consumed their water, there would be no polluted streams, but there would very soon be no streams at all.

What factories do, in effect, is to take the water from

upstream, run it through the factory for their own purposes, and then return it a little farther downstream, more polluted as a result of whatever usage the factory has exacted. Unless the water has been artificially cleaned before its return to the stream, it is dirtier. There would be no point in the diversion of the water unless it were used in some way to cleanse or purify the product, and this means necessarily the dirtying of the water.

Figures differ somewhat as to the nationwide amount of effluent as compared to the amount of sewage. All would place it as more than 50 per cent and some put it as high as 80 per cent. All agree that it is increasing more rapidly than the sewage, and in a few decades will probably equal it in amount. Mere bulk, however, is of secondary importance, as compared with concentration and nature of the pollutants being carried.

No effluents, probably, can be classed as beneficent. They range from comparatively harmless to positively deadly. Soil washed from carrots in a packing plant muddies the water a little, and deposits some silt in the stream; that is not very alarming. Other matter from the same packing plant might include broken scraps of the carrots themselves, and other food-processing plants could contribute a variety of refuse—from whey to the washings that include the blood and offal of slaughtered animals. The effect upon the stream of such matter is about the same as that of sewage. It adds to the load to be carried by the dissolved oxygen, and in too high concentration smothers the stream.

Highly dangerous, and often actively poisonous, are the inorganic effluents. Merely to list them and to identify their sources would require pages. They strain the vocabulary that the ordinary college graduate may have attained from his chemistry course. There are alkalis and acids. There are active poisons such as the arsenic compounds and even the cyanides. There are slower-acting poisons, such as compounds of lead and copper. There are sulfides, sulfites, and fluorides. Of even more deadly import is the host of newly developed "exotic organics," such as many of the pesticides.

In one detail effluents are generally innocent. Unlike sewage, the normal effluent is free of pathogenic organisms. Not even bacteria can live in the stuff.

Entirely aside from any matter of right and wrong, or of good and bad, the problem of factory-effluents shows

the new relationship of man to his environment. Even a
century ago, the environment still seemed almost infinitely
strong. Man moved a little dirt, cut a tree, built a petty
dike, dredged a stream to make it a few feet deeper. Even
yet man is helpless as regards his environment in the
larger sense—the atmosphere, the ocean, and the solar
system. But on land, and particularly with respect to the
streams which flow across the land, he has got the upper
hand. Two centuries ago, man's activities seemed small in
comparison with the river. He could safely, it seemed,
pour into it whatever overflow of odds and ends he happened to accumulate. That era has ended.

That the situation is serious scarcely needs to be further
demonstrated. The situation may even be called critical.
To reform it will be a huge task that will tax (often,
literally), our resources to the limit. We have failed to
consider the basic law of the physics books, and we are
not so rich as we think.

With respect to sewage, the previous chapter attempted
to show that the problem could be considered an opportunity. No such possibility seems to exist with effluents.
Certain economies can doubtless be effected, and some of
these might be made to pay. Such valuable materials as
copper, and even silver, are floating down our stream-
courses, and better methods of control might prevent the
escape of even these minute quantities. Certain byprod-
ucts, also, may be produced. For instance, yeast can be
grown on sulfite, and is even now being thus produced.
The trouble is the market for yeast is definitely limited in
comparison to the amounts of sulfite available as effluent
from paper mills.

A particularly difficult problem arises at the economic
level. In our civilization factories are "good." In fact, the
total amount of effluent in a year could probably be taken
as an index of prosperity. Factories mean jobs. Having
allowed the factories to pollute the streams, we cannot
then, suddenly, suppress the factories in order to clean the
streams.

An especially precarious situation arises with the marginal industry, such as an isolated paper mill, operated by
a small company, narrowly profitable. A preemptory law
demanding that the mill should no longer pollute the
stream would only result in putting the company out of
business. In the larger economic picture such a result
would be reasonable, but it would also mean the near

destruction of the little town now existing on the payroll from the mill. In such a community public opinion is strongly in favor of pollution. These townspeople are a small minority, whose rights should not be ruthlessly suppressed, even though the action can be justified at a higher level.

Still, the whole situation as regards effluence is a hopeful one—indeed, curiously hopeful. There can be a long listing of these hopeful signs.

(1) Factories themselves need moderately clean water. Each factory, except the top one, has a certain interest to the end that the factories farther upstream should not produce too poisonous or dirty an effluent.

(2) Basic law against pollution of streams is well established. We may consider it only strange that it should ever have been otherwise. How did anyone, factory-owner or other, consider himself privileged to use the river as a dump? By that very act, he polluted the water, which was not his own property, but flowed on to someone else. The establishment and the failure of early laws to forbid it merely show how small man once thought himself with respect to nature.

(3) The points at which effluents flow into the streams are comparatively few. In this respect, there is a contrast with sewage. A city of moderate size may have a million toilets, sinks, and so forth, at which sewage originates. It has, however, not more than a few hundred factories. Moreover, these factories are well-known, and operating under licenses. The enforcement of any law about what could be dumped into a toilet or into a sink would be obviously impossible, but the enforcement of law against factory effluents is as simple as enforcement ever gets.

(4) With respect to effluents there is, at a somewhat superficial level, a clear case of public good versus private profit. Again, the contrast exists with sewage, with which the problem is public against public. At times indeed, one public agency may combat another as regards effluents, as when two cities, or the state and national governments, have conflicting laws or differing strictness of enforcement. In general, however, when public good clashes with private profit the political situation in a democracy favors public good. Private profit may buy immunity for a while. Or there may be a special case as in that of the marginal paper-mill just imagined. But public good, once clearly

established, becomes a powerful political issue. When emotions get involved, as they obviously do in connection with stream-pollution, the issue may even become politically inflammable.

(5) Factories, especially as operated by large corporations, are in themselves a part of our affluent society. In normal times, they are prosperous. They can therefore afford to set aside some small part of their income to clean their water. The system permits them to pass this expense on to their customers in increased prices. Moreover, advertising has become an essential part of the activity of the affluent society, and corporations put their faith in advertising. They have recently directed some effort at the general public in an attempt to improve that newly discovered entity, the "corporate image." A steel company runs a double-page advertisement in a national magazine on the crisis in pollution and what that company is doing about it. Everything is there, including "Before" and "After" pictures. Such an advertisement is a good sign for the future.

The situation is also hopeful in that the executives and directors of modern large corporations are usually trained to take the long view and are likely in themselves to be men of parts. Gone, generally speaking, is the crude Silas Lapham of the nineteenth century, and even the gauche George F. Babbitt of the early twentieth century must by now be an old man, on the retired list. In their places, with many companies at least, are men who are trained to think of their corporation as essentially immortal. A mining company acquires reserves of ore which may not be touched within a generation; a lumber company or a paper company plants and tends trees which cannot be harvested for half a century. Moreover, these executives and directors are Americans who wish to enjoy their own country. Many of them are anglers and duck-hunters, and the sight and smell of a ruined stream are just as depressing to them as to anyone else.

These men, too, live in fear of government regulation, and sometimes this fear seems to approach the point of obsession. Above all, they wish to escape regulation in the big things such as prices, production, and wages. As compared with such major matters, pollution is very small. So, prudentially speaking, they prefer to clean up pollution before the government steps in. In that way, the government will not set a precedent of regulation and may avoid the habit.

On the other hand, we cannot be complaisant about the virtues of large corporations. Some black sheep exist among them. The situation was recently emphasized by Secretary of the Interior Stewart Udall, one of the many eminent political figures to be deeply concerned over pollution. He recently nominated a large paper company of Detroit to head the list of the country's dirty industries. Symbolical, we may perhaps consider it, that this Queen of Filth is largely involved in the manufacture of toilet tissue.

(6) As the chapter title has suggested, affluence seems naturally to combat effluence. We might even say that there is a kind of built-in control, though it has been slow, admittedly, to take effect.

Affluence gives a chance for leisure and recreation. When people were working seventy-two hours a week, they were not likely to care about the condition of a stream. But, with affluence, they gain time, cash, and energy to go fishing, swimming, shooting, water-skiing, sailing, and motor-boating, on weekends or even after work. The situation would certainly be ironic if this chance for fun, just when it has arisen, should be ruined by the pollution of streams and lakes. There is every evidence that the public is aroused.

Moreover, the public displays an emotional intensity in the matter. The feeling seems to go somewhat beyond practicality. In the defilement of their rivers and lakes, the American people feel also a personal and psychological defilement.

(7) As a final reason to be hopeful, one can point to some spectacular successes. A cause that holds hope for victory is always a more popular one than that other which offers only hard fighting and a drawn battle.

Wyoming supplies a story of success, with its North Platte. As is usually true, both sewage and effluents were involved. This river, like so many others, has a historic linkage with the heroic American past. The old trappers' trail through South Pass followed it, and along that trail the covered-wagon emigrants, their oxen's heads pointed for Oregon and California, broke out a road for the West. Where the city of Casper now stands, was then the dangerous crossing of the North Platte, where wagons were rafted and oxen were swum, and where the rolling stream sometimes swept away both animals and people.

In 1948, the U.S. Public Health Service reported that the river below Casper, for 150 miles, was so badly polluted with sewage and refinery effluence that "it is doubtful if recovery can ever be obtained." People reported that they could sometimes smell the river from three or four miles away. The effluents included oil, carbolic acid, sulfides, and salts of calcium and magnesium.

By the middle fifties, however, counter-action had begun, and public opinion was being aroused. The order in which the different offenders began to spend money is significant—first, the big corporations; second, the municipalities; third, the small operators.

The big corporations were the oil companies, some of them engaged in business over much of the world at the billion-dollar level. To the directors of such a company the abatement of a bad smell in the refinery at Casper, Wyoming, looms as little more than an adjustment in petty cash. What if it costs a few million? The new oil-field in Venezuela is developing nicely, and the GNP of Australia shows a promising rise. The expense of fixing things at Casper will be absorbed into the general budget with scarcely a visible ripple. So, by 1957, the big oil companies had made much progress, and the amount of effluent being dumped into the river was falling off rapidly.

Only by this time did the citizens of Casper get around to passing a bond issue for the treatment of their sewage, and even later than this the smaller communities took action.

Last of all to cooperate were the small companies and the individual operators. To them, the new capital-expenditure was a serious matter, and they could hardly be blamed for refusing to act until they were required to do so.

The ending, as reported after a few years, has almost the glamorous perfection of the fairy tale "—and they all lived happily ever after." Fish rise in the stream, and people swim there. One area, reserved for the dumping of effluents, has turned out to be a game refuge. Some industries are discovering that they can make use, to some extent, of what they were previously letting run away, and one of the small companies reports a handsome income from a byproduct. Property values along the river have risen many times over. . . .

Nothing is pleasanter to record than a success story. But nature and time play tricks, and clever solutions sometimes turn out to be not so clever. The idyllic situation on the North Platte may develop troubles in twenty or thirty years. As for nature biting the hand of the beneficent engineer, let us consider what happened at Denver. . . .

There was, it seems, a government arsenal which was manufacturing something-or-other, which gave rise to a particularly nasty and dangerous effluent. To put this vile liquid where it could do no possible harm, the ingenious engineers drilled a hole, thousands of feet into the earth. At that depth there was a permeable stratum into which, the experts believed, the nasty effluent would diffuse and never be heard from again, until perhaps, after some hundreds of millions of years, when a new geological era would have begun. So they poured the effluent down the hole, and all seemed well.

Then, curiously, the city of Denver began to have earthquakes. They were not serious ones, but they alarmed people considerably. Who knew but that the quakes might grow stronger? During some weeks or months, there would be earthquakes, and then they would stop for a while.

The geologists, naturally, became interested. After a year or so, one of them was able to make a simple coordination. Soon after the time when effluent was poured into the deep hole, he discovered, there were earthquakes. When nothing was being poured in, the earthquakes soon stopped. The tremendous pressure exerted by such a high column of liquid even if the liquid itself was not of great quantity, was enough to disturb the balance of the rocks. . . .

In any great and long-continuing war—and the contest of civilization with pollution may be so compared—there are at any moment certain quiescent sectors and others that blaze up. In the year 1966, stream-pollution, especially from effluents, was highly active. Even more than smog, it involved all parts of the country, and came home, as Bacon put it "to men's business and bosoms"—or, we might put it more pointedly—to their eyes and nostrils.

The general perturbation involved the citizens both of cities and of rural districts. It became a grass-roots movement. Newspapers and popular magazines ran special articles. A politician had no need to put an ear to the ground; the uproar was plain, even in the national capital.

Of all the battle sectors, that involving Lake Erie and its tributary streams was the largest and hottest. Journalists of the lake cities alternated between blaming things on the rival cities, and beating their own breasts in open shame. There was advocacy of boycott against offending companies. In June, Secretary of the Interior Udall visited Cleveland, declared the Cuyahoga to be the dirtiest river he had ever seen, and stated that Lake Erie was "the best test case we have." In August President Johnson himself spoke at Buffalo, and then took a short voyage on the lake. He declared the purpose of his trip to be to take the profit out of poverty and put sparkle back in the Great Lakes.

In this same summer an interstate conference, involving five states and the Federal government, sat and deliberated. Perhaps even more significant was a hearing of the State Water Resources Commission of Michigan at which the representatives of twenty-one villages and townships were asked to appear. In July, at the other end of the political scale, the Senate passed a vast anti-pollution bill, with Senator Muskie predicting that one hundred billion dollars would be needed before long.

In September came a helicopter tour over the waters around Detroit for fifty observers, including members of the House Subcommittee on Natural Resources and Power. The views were described as colorful, but lacking in blue. Where the lake should have been blue, it was largely green from algae. Near the mouths of the rivers the color varied from black to brown, with streaks of creamy green and spots of yellow tinged with purple, along with patches of milky white and chalky gray. (A Detroit journalist, writing about the same time, emphasized the shades of orange.)

That summer, on the Fourth of July, without discrimination as to American and Canadian sides of the lake, the temperatures went up to 100 degrees. But the beaches were not crowded, and few had the stomach to enter the water, which was almost opaque, because of tiny plants, and other things you could not see individually. Around the edge of the water there was green slime, and an occasional dead fish—but most of the fish had died in previous years. . . .

Streams, by their very nature, change their water rapidly, and thus respond soon, once the sources of poisoning are removed. Some stream bottoms have been so greatly altered that recovery will be slow, and in a few streams a kind of permanent damage may have been produced. On the whole, however, as the case of the North Platte demonstrates, there is a basis of optimism with streams. We must remember, of course, that the North Platte is a comparatively small and rapid river, quick to respond to simple and not very expensive remedies.

Estuaries, like rivers, provide circulation of water, by tides and currents. For these and other reasons, they also may show quick recovery.

Lakes provide the worst problem. They are tideless, and their bulk of water is usually vast, as compared with the in-flow and out-flow. A droplet of water, once in a lake, may be expected, on the average, to remain there for a long time. In some natural backwater it may remain indefinitely, until it happens to be evaporated out. As a result, in many lakes there exists nothing that corresponds to a current pronounced enough to effect a change of water.

Of Lake Erie, one expert merely shakes his head and declares vaguely that the cure will take years. Another suggests five centuries, if it is just let alone from this time on. Still another declares of the lake's growth of algae, "We simply don't know, yet, how to get rid of it." . . .

This chapter and the preceding one have dealt with related subjects. Though sewage and factory effluents differ in origin and composition, both are waterborne and both show their malignant effects in streams, lakes, and tidal waters. In conclusion, therefore, they cannot be separated—in discussion, any more than in actuality.

Not to be forgotten, in connection with water pollution, is also the whole crisis of water-shortage. Conversion of seawater is the optimistic hope of many people. But such conversion is expensive, and is hardly practical at all for regions distant from the sea. Moreover, what is lacking is often not water, but good water. The shortage, therefore, may be overcome, it would seem, by maintaining pure streams, rather than by the much more difficult process of desalting seawater and pumping it to Montana or Kansas.

The most critical part of the duplex situation probably involves the factory effluents, many of which are actual poisons. On the other hand, the most difficult of solution is the problem of overfertilization, as created by the accumulation of sewage, even of treated sewage, in lakes. Of all the pollutants thus involved the phosphates are the most tenacious.

In such a situation two conclusions are inevitable. First, special efforts should be taken to insure that no other lakes are thus permanently polluted. Second, much time and money should be channeled into research so that the expert *can* know what to do about it. . . .

The whole idea of affluence providing a built-in resistance to effluence, as suggested in this chapter, may be a too optimistic one. If we grant basically, however, that stream pollution, however caused, must be halted, the question then arises as to how, in our system, the payments are to be met.

The very size of the bill itself can hardly as yet be estimated, but there can be no doubt but that it will be high. The governor of Michigan recently declared that his state alone must expect to spend, in the next ten years, the sum of nine hundred million dollars to control (he did not put it "to end") the pollution of waters. A comparable bill for the whole country might therefore be put at forty billion. And this expenditure would not suggest the end of expense or a total victory.

As to who is going to pay, the answer is basically simple. Our civilization is going to pay. It will foot the bill for two reasons—first, to keep the United States from becoming a place where its millions of inhabitants cannot live in decency and health; second, to create an environment where they can live with a reasonable degree of happiness.

Eventually the charge will fall back upon the public. If the factory-owners pay the immediate charges, they will only, in a system of free enterprise, pass them back to the public in increased prices. If part of the bill is met by taxes, such a procedure will merely put the charge more immediately upon the public. Some easing of the blow, by tax-expedients, may be necessary to protect marginal operations which should be preserved on social and regional grounds.

In any case the situation as a whole is rapidly passing beyond the point of argument. It is becoming a case of "Clean up or perish!" Billions of the national income will have to be spent to retrieve the streams, lakes, and estuaries from their present befoulment, and billions more in the yearly charge to keep them passably clean. These charges must be figured along with those necessary to prevent their ruin from being used as conduits for sewage. The only alternative is a national disaster which will be infinitely more expensive, in the long run, not only in money, but also in terms of well-being and happy living.

6

GARBAGE

Nobody loves garbage

TWO CHAPTERS have presented the situation as regards water-borne effluvia. The next five chapters will present the land-disposal waste—garbage, junk, litter, agricultural refuse, and mineral refuse.

Land—mere surface per person—is one of a nation's two or three basic resources. Space, openness, and "elbow-room" have been a part of the American heritage, ever since the frontiersman began to think of moving because he could see the smoke from a neighbor's chimney. Our land-surface is not increasing and cannot increase, and every year the share available to each citizen grows less, because of the increase in population. In addition, the space actually available is shrinking because of its preemption by highways, landing-fields, private reservations of a thousand kinds, and garbage dumps—whether or not politely masked under the term "sanitary land-fill."

In contrast to the almost acute excitement about the pollution of the American waters, there is, comparatively, a surprising lack of concern about the pollution of the American land. But, like the waters, the land too is being threatened with destruction in terms of decent living. For instance, the land-surface of the nation is now cluttered with an estimated 200,000 dumps for refuse of various kinds—all of them unsightly, many of them nauseating. Most of these are based upon little planning, and exist under little supervision. They represent the ugly and odorous debris of daily living, hastily and carelessly shoveled into a corner of the room.

Here and there, indeed, the citizens of some municipal districts are beginning to realize that time is running out for nineteenth-century methods of garbage disposal. There is a kind of general concern about litter, but few people have been enough moved to do much about it. The accumulation of junk, especially of automobile hulks, is viewed as an annoyance, but scarcely more.

Nonetheless, we are approaching a crisis with our land—perhaps in a decade. The country is large, and some extensive open spaces still exist. Unfortunately, these do little good for disposal. The production of waste occurs in cities, where the least space for disposal is available. A hundred empty square miles of western desert, or a thousand of northern tundra—neither is of any help, with the cost of transportation what it is. Our urban districts are therefore in the process of burying themselves under their own effluvia. . . .

From the point of view of the ordinary citizen, garbage may be defined as what goes into the can. The average city-dweller produces more than half a ton of it yearly. The emptying of the garbage cans of a city of a million inhabitants therefore amounts to a tonnage that anyone can more easily calculate with a pencil than really appreciate in terms of mass or odor.

Moreover, other urban solid wastes are closely allied to garbage in their composition and in their problem of disposal. Here, for instance, are grass cuttings and the prunings from street-plantings and from parks, in actual tonnage about equal to garbage.

First of all, and most essentially, garbage consists of food-remnants—the scrapings of plates, soured milk, grease from cooking, stale bread, peelings, spoiled fruit, wilted lettuce leaves, and much else equally given to quick decay and the emission of a sour smell. Along with food-leavings, as a second component, go food-containers, rarely clean, still harboring enough food or drink to attract flies and to create odor. Into the can thus go bottles, jars, wrapping paper(greasy with pork chops), paper bags, tin cans (with traces of baked beans and tomato soup), paper containers for frozen foods (no longer frozen). The third component consists of all the cleanings of the house or apartment, the disgorgement of the dustpan and the vacuum cleaner. From this one fraction, the British have, in fact, taken a name for the whole, and called it "dust."

· The fourth and final component, if a mere heterogeneous collection can be called a component, consists of a whole miscellany of solid and semi-solid objects, having as their only common qualities that they are no longer wanted and are small enough to go into the can. Here we have, to catalog a few—old electric light bulbs (sometimes broken), pencil stubs and pencil sharpenings, cuttings and prunings of the potted geranium or African violet, wilted bunches of flowers and faded corsages, the cleanings of bird cages, paper (junk mail, crumpled letters, magazines, some newspapers), used paper handkerchiefs, the dumpings of ashtrays, worn-out shoes and clothes, squeezed tubes of toothpaste, "sanitary" napkins (scarcely any longer so to be distinguished), the puppy's "mess," used contraceptive devices, a dead kitten, the miscellaneous emptyings of wastebaskets, ashes.

By and large, the mixture is perhaps more disgusting and equally as dangerous as is sewage. Moreover, it suffers from the ordinary difficulty of mixtures, that is, the whole is "degraded" to the level of the "lowest" component. An old electric light bulb or a discarded magazine, in itself, is not disgusting. Yet, in the garbage cans they become no more attractive than the putrefying materials that are smeared over them.

The distinguishing qualities of garbage may therefore be said to be two. (1) It has a considerable "unpleasant" or "disgusting" fraction of once edible material that in a period of hours begins to rot and smell, and to attract flies and rats, and thus to become a public-health hazard. (2) Also, mingled with the putrescible material is the much larger bulking part of garbage, such components as metal, glass, plastic, paper, and ashes, which are highly resistant or even impervious to all processes of natural dissolution. Yet, by being thus mingled with the decaying part, they prevent the whole from being treated in the methods which have been developed for sewage.

Though no Thucydides or Gibbon has devoted his historiographical talents to garbage, its story does not remain altogether mysterious. In its antiquity as a disposal problem, it may be granted an honorable third place, following those of the disposal of dead bodies, and of the materials now comprehended under "sewage." Food-leavings, indeed, existed from the very beginning. Man is classified as omnivorous, but he has never been 100 per cent omnivorous. The ancient Norse story of *Loki* who won an eating contest by devouring the wooden container along with the food is only explicable as an allegory that *Loki* is fire. Even Neanderthal man, for all his massive jaw, could not eat the larger bones, along with such other materials as hides, husks, shells, and rinds. Moreover, primitive man often existed by a feast-and-famine regime. When he was in luck, he ate only the best parts, and left the rest to lie around and rot. Then he solved the problem of garbage by moving away to a new camp ground. Moreover, in ordinary times, his scavenging helpmates aided him considerably, and man gradually learned to appreciate the sanitary services rendered by the dog, the pig, and the domestic fowl.

During the many centuries of earlier civilization, no serious garbage problem existed, for reasons sufficiently explained in an introductory chapter. Historical records shed only incidental and accidental light on the whole question.

One such reference makes clear that the heaps sometimes got rather high. In 1415, when the Portuguese were attacking Ceuta, two Portuguese princes gallantly charged up a dominating mound, which seemed to be a strategic point. They later discovered (possibly from the smell) that they had thus heroically captured the city dump.

The actual word *garbage* is distinctively of the English language. In fact, the use of different words in the modern European languages indicates that the conception itself arose so late that no general Germanic or Romance term could establish itself.

In English the word dates from the Middle Ages, but its meaning was different. It was originally a term of cookery! The garbage of a fowl meant what was later known as giblets, a term which, like garbage, has itself almost vanished from culinary nomenclature. This comprehensive term included such "insides," as liver, gizzard, and heart. Delectable viands could be concocted from them, but they were also subject, either cooked or uncooked, to rapid and noisome spoilage. A shift of meaning is therefore explicable, and it had happened by Shakespeare's time.

The problem of disposal, however, failed to become serious until after the growth of cities, and of at least a certain affluence that accompanied the Industrial Revolution. By the middle of the nineteenth century London and other great concentrations were feeling a certain strain. In Dickens's *Our Mutual Friend* some of the action is involved with great heaps of "dust," which had once been beyond the inhabited area but had eventually become an unsightly clutterment.

British and continental cities largely introduced the so-called destructor system, by which garbage was burned and steam produced. Under favorable circumstances the process could even be made to pay, and at least it got rid of much of the material, though it still left a considerable bulk of ashes and noncombustibles, in addition to smoke and fumes. Some American cities, chiefly in the crowded northeastern coastal plain, have also made use of incinerators.

On the whole, however, as American cities grew out of frontier villages, no real system developed. The whole procedure seems to operate on a basis that can only be described by the help of hyphens as hit-or-miss, year-to-year, and hand-to-mouth.

A recent report to the President estimates that only one half of the American cities "currently have satisfactory refuse disposal systems." Even what is meant by "satisfactory" is probably to be very leniently interpreted, and what the unsatisfactory cities are doing or not doing had better be left unexpressed. Essentially, in the whole field, as the same report expresses the situation, things have "not moved very far from the invention of the garbage pail and the city dump."

As with sewage, the whole process splits into collection and disposal. Again as with sewage, the process of collection is working, in a somewhat archaic and shaky manner, but the process of disposal is raising difficulties. . . .

Though there has been, we may agree, little progress and certainly no technical breakthrough since the invention of the garbage pail, that implement in itself continues to work. The popularization of the garbage-disposal unit has produced an alternate, but even it demands time of the housewife. Moreover, this handy unit still leaves some material for the garbage can, and some housewives do not feel the device to be worth the extra complication. In any case, as long as our social structure rests upon the individual family unit and the private preparation of food, there seems to be no solution but that the one responsible for the housework must include the disposal of "urban solid waste" as part of the duties. Indeed, the can itself demands a certain amount of care and cleansing.

The next step involves the garbage-truck. On the whole, it seems to work well enough. In most cities the trucks are well painted, make a good appearance, and are associated with only a minimal smell. The old riddle, "What has four wheels and flies?" is hardly applicable any longer. . . .

The real difficulty arises with the question of where the truck is to dump its laboriously collected materials. What mechanism next takes charge? "This," as the epic poet sang in another connection, "This is the labor, this the burden."

There are almost as many ways of attempting to get rid of garbage as there are cities making the attempt. Not only are there several basic methods, with some submethods, but there are also an almost infinite number of variations, adaptations, and combinations of methods. The material itself is of such multiverse nature that a single method of disposal seldom suffices. Most of the procedures are traditional and crude, smack of the nineteenth century, and utterly fail to grapple with the Law of the Conservation of Matter.

(1) Among the still-approved methods is that of burning. In a well-constructed municipal incinerator, burning has much to recommend it. But it is expensive; it makes use of the atmosphere as a dump; it leaves residues of ashes and noncombustibles that amount to about half of the original mass.

Open burning at dumps produces more smoke, and consumes only a small fraction of the whole. It means, essentially, mere dumping rather than burning.

Incineration at the source, that is, in the home, is not much practiced, and offers little possibility.

(2) Traditional disposal usually meant feeding the garbage to animals. In the nineteenth century the method continued, chiefly with municipal hog farms. Some threat from trichinosis developed, but this responsibility could be pushed off upon the consumer, who was advised to cook his pork thoroughly. Unfortunately, the feeding of garbage was found to spread vesicular exanthema, a deadly disease for hogs. An industry can take chances at killing a few consumers, but it cannot take chances with killing very many of its prime suppliers. Laws had to be passed requiring the sterilization of garbage, thus to kill the organisms of exanthema, and also, incidentally, those of trichinosis.

But sterilization of garbage costs money, and the margin of profit of the industry decreased until, in many instances, it vanished.

Besides, there were positive objections to the hog farms. True, the system produced some meat, and thus represented a recycling of the organic material. But the farms circulated a pungent and wide-spreading odor. So they had to be pushed farther away from inhabited areas, still with increased costs of haulage.

In addition, the system took no account of the basic problem of matter. Ingenious agricultural statisticians estimated that a hog, at top efficiency, put on one pound a day by eating six pounds of garbage. What then must happen to the other five pounds? Some of it returned to the atmosphere as carbon dioxide, and as other gases, by unmentionable processes. But most of the five pounds, actually increased because of the water that the hog had drunk, piled up as manure.

Essentially, thus, the system disposed of only a small proportion of the material by recycling. It was merely a process of transforming garbage into manure, and such a procedure can be reckoned advantageous only if you prefer manure to garbage. Most people would count this a hard choice, and modern agricultural economics seems to agree. When agriculture came to depend more upon commercial fertilizers, manure was a less needed commodity. Therefore, as the twentieth century advanced, the feeding of garbage to hogs declined, until it is now disappearing entirely from a highly urbanized civilization.

(3)   Mere dumping, crude as it is, has always been, and still remains, the simplest and commonest means of disposal of garbage. As long as land is cheap enough, the dump can be large and far enough isolated. "Collect-haul-dump" can then represent the whole process, and the minimal expense. Rats and flies raise problems, but they can be controlled, although they may sometimes not be.

The small towns and even the small cities may be able to continue with this cheapest of methods. Some of the great urban districts still rely on it essentially. Its time, however, seems definitely to be running out. Metropolitan centers begin to be surrounded by satellite cities, and then in turn by suburban districts. Land values soar. There is simply no room for garbage dumps, unless the trucks go many miles afield, and the expense of the long haul becomes prohibitive. Some large cities have already reached a point of crisis. Others can see into the future for ten years or a little more, but such a span of time is negligible in the life of a city. Unsightly, smelly, increasingly expensive with rising land-values, doubtfully sanitary, the open dump offers no hope.

(4)　Composting may be considered a step or two in advance of open dumping. It is, unfortunately, more expensive in many ways, although it consumes less land. It demands the separation of putrescible material from the rest of the mass. This material, that which we consider the garbage proper, is piled and allowed to decay into inoffensive compost. The compost then can be transferred to the fields. The method offers some possibilities for the future, but it cannot be a total solution.

(5)　Disposal at sea can only be available for coastal communities. But civilization itself has been described as a growth along the edge of salt water, and many millions of Americans live near the ocean or on navigable waters connecting with it. Moreover, the ocean is the natural sink of the world, so great in bulk that even civilized man cannot yet be concerned about polluting it with garbage. The chief trouble is that much garbage floats, and is likely to be drifted back to the shore while still in the process of decaying. To take it so far out that it will not drift back is expensive, and creates difficult problems in periods of stormy weather.

Various experiments have been conducted, and are being continued. In straightforward and typically American manner, the mere application of force has been tried, in an attempt to compress garbage to the point at which it will be heavier than sea-water and so sink docilely to the bottom. One such experiment has attained a measure of success, though the expense of the installation and operation of pressing machinery is far from negligible. The experimenters, however, were given pause by a horrible thought. Though compressed, the garbage still remained organic and subject to decay. In the course of months or years, gas might generate, and the compressed masses would then disintegrate, come floating gaily to the surface, and drift shoreward, where surf-bathers would find themselves swimming among last year's plate-scrapings.

Some other beginnings of disposal at sea may be considered tentatively successful. Some fruit-packing companies on San Francisco Bay load refuse into a good-sized barge, which is eventually towed fifty miles beyond the Golden

Gate and pumped out. Most of the material is liquid or semiliquid and mingles quickly with the sea-water. The peach-pits and apple-peelings float off, and cannot be traced far, though no one knows just what becomes of them. They may act as a fertilizer, and become food for plankton. Some of the pits may eventually wash up on the beaches of the Philippines.

With the land becoming more and more crowded, and with the ocean still as vast and uninhabited as ever, disposal of garbage at sea offers a tempting possibility. Obviously, it should be developed along with careful experiment.

(6)   By and large, as of the present time, the most advanced method of disposal for large cities is that known as sanitary fill, or "dump-and-cover." It is essentially a sophisticated version of the old open dumping, and superior in many ways. There is no burning, and therefore no problem of smoke or smog. Odors are so minimal as hardly to create a difficulty, and the erection of a high fence removes most of the "eye-blight."

In such an operation, bulldozers clear off the soil to permit the trucks to dump the garbage, and then the bulldozers push the soil back on top. At the end of every working day, all the dumped garbage is covered so that rats have no chance. In addition the earth is tamped down and made impermeable to fly-larvae. Such nuisances as blowing newspapers do not escape beyond the fence, and can be retrieved.

Offering little public offense, dump-and-cover creates much less protest from residents of an area than does open dumping, and so does not require such isolation. Therefore it does not so soon come up against the problem of crowding. Eventually, however, it must.

In one curious way, dump-and-fill actually helps to create eventual space, not to destroy it. The land thus treated is not suitable for the building of homes for a long period of years. As subterranean decay proceeds slowly, the earth inevitably settles, and from time to time the discharges of ill-smelling and even explosive gases break through to the surface. No one wants to have his house develop cracks from settling, nor does he want his rooms to be intermittently permeated by a stench, or occasionally to explode when he is only trying to light a cigarette. But a little settling does not hurt a golf course, and in the breezes of a public park an occasional mingling of gas can pass unnoticed. Dump-and-cover may thus be preserving the open spaces of the next generation. But by the very fact that it is demanding of space the system of dump-and-cover cannot clearly point the way ahead. . . .

To sum up, the very existence of so many "systems" is in itself an indication that there is no really satisfactory one. None of the six works very well, and combinations fail to work much better. All are expensive.

Even so, they rarely face the problem of recycling or of ultimate disposal. Collectively and in gross, the American cities seem merely to follow the individual housewife's lead by just getting rid of the disgusting stuff as soon as possible, without inquiring about what becomes of it eventually. . . .

As to what should be done, the first answer is that much more money should be expended on research and experiment. As compared with the wealthy sewage research, the investigation of the problem of solid wastes has been a poor relation. Every university and every health department has its expert on sewage, but experts on solid wastes are rare. Only in the last few years has some money been channeled in that direction. In general, "sanitary engineer" has meant a specialist on the problems of sewage and water pollution.

Something also should be done with the development of what might be called palliatives, though such easy-going methods are seldom congenial to the American liking for direct and decisive attack.

One palliative that has actually proved popular for other reasons is the garbage-grinder in the sink. By making more of the garbage water-borne, it simplifies the problem somewhat. Eventually the grinders will handle some paper and much else that they cannot now undertake. Even so, they can probably never dispose of more than half of the load, and so cannot provide a full solution. At the same time, unfortunately, the garbage-grinder increases the demands upon the water supply, and at best merely turns garbage into sewage, a procedure that can only be considered good if the sewage itself can then be properly and economically processed.

Affluence also, without design, is supplying another palliative. Greater use of frozen and of fresh foods reduces and will doubtless continue to reduce the troublesome glass and metal content of solid waste.

In general, however, affluence intensifies the problem.

The American manufacturer and retailer, for instance, have gone mad over packaging, and have taken the American housewife along. Packaging materials total a yearly value of twenty billion dollars. Even the simplest product has to be wrapped like the queen's jewels. A few ounces of crackers are encased first in wax paper, and next in a cardboard box and are then put into an individual paper bag. The weight of the wrapping may be more than the weight of the crackers. Then the reverse process has to be set up, and all this weight of paper has to be taken away, via garbage can and truck.

The so-called junk mail raises a similar problem. First, the Post Office Department usually has to carry this mass of unsolicited advertisement at a loss. Next, most of it goes into the wastebasket immediately, often without even being opened. Then it too must start the long and expensive road back, at public expense. Higher rates for certain classes of mail could certainly be justified because of the disposal problem.

Other possible palliatives can be treated later in connection with the related problem of litter. . . .

That mythical "someone" who devotes himself to the coinage of "well-known sayings" has recently been quoted in a description of American society: "We are standing knee-deep in garbage, throwing rockets at the moon." Even if the garbage is no more than ankle-deep, the situation is bad enough, and in many cities it is at the point of becoming acute.

Certain expedients, already indicated, seem to offer alleviation, but no real solution.

Separation of the various components at the home has been tried, and is still in practice here and there. To separate putrescible matter from non-putrescible by the use of two garbage cans is not beyond the mental capacity of the average housewife. Some cities have even required three cans.

But the practice has been unpopular with housewives, and no one blames them greatly. The regulations are difficult to enforce, and so chiselers have their chance. The conscientious housewife feels put upon. From the point of view of our society as a whole, moreover, the practice seems out-of-date and inefficient. It depends upon hand labor in an age devoted to power machinery. Why should society put this additional responsibility upon the already hard-worked wife and mother?

Palliatives aside, the general line of development seems to suggest that the collection of garbage may be left about as it is. The change in treatment will occur after the material has been gathered into its mixed and putrescent mass. At that point machine labor can take over.

Grinding, flotation, and other methods can separate the organic material that is subject to decay. It can be added to the sewage, and treated with it. Or, being vastly less in mass than the sewage, it can be handled separately. Either as added to the sewage or as treated alone, it can be considered a resource. Destructive distillation, for instance, can convert it into various useful products. Even if such processing can never be profitable in itself, it will serve the essential function of recycling the material and thus, in the best and fullest sense of the words, disposing of it.

The non-putrescible mass of the garbage, by much the larger fraction both by bulk and by weight, can in its turn be subjected to further large-scale separation. Iron and steel scraps can be magnetically removed. The creative imaginations of scientists and technologists still must grapple with the problem of how, economically by mass methods, they may separate one from another such miscellaneous materials as glass, aluminum foil, paper, plastics, ashes, wood, and the dozens of others. Indeed, complete separation may not be necessary. In any case, modern expertise has undertaken and solved what seem to be much more difficult tasks.

The end-point, with the non-putrescible materials also, would seem to be recycling. Countless tons of glass bottles, instead of being piled somewhere to produce a monstrous and never-to-vanish clutter, would then be passed back into circulation, either as bottles to be sterilized and refilled, or as glass to be melted and refashioned.

By hard work, mental and mechanical, some solution will have to be worked out to prevent the garbage level from rising inch-by-inch—from ankle to knee and upward. We shall have to pay liberally, but to escape being bogged we should be reconciled to payment, even if we cannot be expected to be happy about it. Possibly the income from salvage may be greater than now seems likely.

Figures on the present cost of garbage disposal are hard to come by. They tend to get mixed up with other costs. Possibly a sum of three billion dollars annually is reasonable. Such a figure includes no reckoning for the millions of hours expended by housewives, and by people in small towns who haul their own garbage to the dump. Whatever the figure now is, it should be larger. It will be larger in the future. . . .

Still another suggestion smacks of despair—or almost a "sick" humor. It involves making a kind of virtue of necessity. We are destined to have mountains of garbage. Very well, then, make mountains out of them. Much of our populous Middle West is lamentably lacking in high elevations, but is producing abundant garbage. Select, therefore, a spot about halfway between Chicago and Detroit, and pile all the garbage there. The mound will rise rapidly. It will, as a few years pass, engulf a village or two, but that is the price of progress. Eventually, though no one seems as yet to have figured the exact year, work on this mound can be ended. We shall have then a fine eminence. A funicular takes people to the top and they sit there, drink beer, and enjoy the view. In fact, by throwing the beer cans over the railing they can continue to add to the mountain. The winter possibilities for skiing are obvious. One single problem seems to remain. What public figure should we select whose name would fittingly be bestowed upon this mountain of garbage?

7

JUNK

*"Don't shoot the
secondary-materials man!"*

A TYPICAL AMERICAN CITY now displays—like a fair-sized hill or a minor mountain—its heap of discarded automobile hulks. The effect upon the American public of these heaps has been profound, curious, and out of all proportion to reality. "Shocking!" is a common reaction. But why, in the face of such gargantuan problems as those of sewage and garbage, should people be so concerned about some piles of metal? Old automobile bodies neither emit an odor, nor do they trouble the ears with noise, nor do they spread disease. Aesthetically, to the eye, they are rather more pleasing than the grimy urban districts in which they are usually found. To understand the depth of this reaction, we must, apparently, delve into some psychological recesses. But, to do so, we must consider the subject of junk in general. . . .

Like most of the related terms, *junk* is vague in meaning. It is like the non-putrescible fraction of garbage, except that it consists of material too bulky or objects too large to be squeezed into the can. Size, not kind, is of the essence. A small transistor radio goes out as garbage; a large set goes as junk. From that point the size ranges upward to old cars and trucks, and eventually to old locomotives, airplanes, and steamships. So also, paper bags and wrappers, along with scattered newspapers, go into the can, but waste paper in bulk and newspapers in bundles are an important element in junk. Just as junk cannot altogether be distinguished from garbage, so also it is only differentiated from *trash* and *rubbish* in a vague manner. As opposed to these two, junk implies a possible re-use.

Thus conceived, junk is the basis of many thriving businesses. There is even an association of such businesses, but in the interest, or imagined interest, of public relations, the junk-dealers are organized as the National Association of Secondary Material Industries. The subdivisions of this association indicate the chief materials of their commerce, that is, the Paper Stock Institute, the Textile Division, the Scrap Rubber and Plastic Institute, and three institutes or divisions dividing among themselves the enormous commerce in metal scrap.

Junk, both as a conception and as a term, has little history behind it. The word itself, traditionally existing only in the English language, may be traced from the fifteenth century, when it meant an old and worn rope. A seaman's term, it was probably derived from the Portuguese, in their century of notable achievement in seafaring. *Junca* means a reed in Portuguese, and of reeds a kind of cheap and inferior rope was made. Such ropes did not wear long, and so the derogatory suggestion of the word easily developed. Once worn out, these ropes were cut up to serve for oakum or boat-fenders, and *junk* thus began to assume its modern suggestion of "secondary material." By the eighteenth century, British and American seamen were applying the word in a general derogatory sense, as when salt-beef was called junk. It was also used for miscellaneous collections of worn, secondhand, and cheap goods. Shops which stocked such materials for the outfitting of seamen came to be called junk shops. Only toward the end of the nineteenth century, however, first in the United States and later in Great Britain, did the word begin to assume its modern meaning—used material, of a certain bulk and durability, chiefly conceived by the consumer as something to be got rid of, but salvable under favorable circumstances.

Junk, therefore, is something new and characteristic of our own time. The future archaeologist will reconstruct this civilization from the rich harvest of junk heaps. The present archaeologist, studying the past, has no such chance. The chief material of which he can make use is the plentiful supply of broken pots. Even these, we can suppose, were often mended instead of being thrown away. A thoroughly broken pot, however, was apparently beyond salvage, even in the poverty-stricken days of the early historical period. First the Industrial Revolution and then the Age of Affluence have combined to produce junk.

In the United States we may place the later nineteenth century as the early junk period, extending over into the twentieth century in the quieter portions of our country. People may even grow sentimental and nostalgic about that period. Wallace Stegner, in his *Wolf Willow*, revisits the village dump of his youth, and from it evokes much of the spirit of earlier times. Those were the years of what we might call the intimate and inoffensive dump. Moreover, that was the period of the house with the attic, and much of what would have been hauled away as junk was merely taken up to the attic, there to rest for a generation until it could be recycled as antiques.

Any older American may grow nostalgic, remembering the junkman who used to come along the street with a bony horse pulling a ramshackle wagon, and calling out his desire to buy almost anything. Frugal housewives did not disdain him; small boys carried to him the bottles that they had collected.

In such a connection the present writer recalls that his own first self-employment was in the junk business. (If he had stayed with it, he might be richer than he is now.) The small town where he lived was having some water-pipes laid, and the ditches, with walls much higher than a boy's head, were romantic places through which to wander. The boy made a discovery, and no Forty-niner was ever more elated. The iron pipes were sealed by having molten lead poured into their joints. There was a certain amount of wastage, and the boy found that here and there he could pick this solidified lead from the gravel with which it had mingled. He collected the wastage, melted it on the kitchen stove in an iron skillet, skimmed off the earth and pebbles, and poured the lead into a baking-powder can. Finally he sold it to a junkman, and may have got as much as a dollar for it—very good money by small-boy standards, as of then. Those were the simple days when labor costs still did not loom so large in comparison with the prices of such materials as metals.

In later years, the destiny of the writer often required that he should follow for long distances the old emigrant trail to California. The records were eloquent of the hundreds of wagons abandoned in the desert. Granted that the wood of these wagons might disappear in a hundred years, why was there not more scrap metal lying around, such as trace-chains, horseshoes, and fittings of all kinds? The reason, he finally discovered, was that junk-gatherers, many of them Chinese, went out along the trail with their wagons, finding it profitable to salvage all that old iron.

In the course of these exploratory trips along the trail, the author often passed isolated ranch houses. Such places no longer consist of a log house and a horse corral. Instead, each is likely to be surrounded by a most depressing junkyard. This being the age of agricultural machinery, the rancher buys his machinery and hauls it in, many miles. Wornout or superseded after a few years, it is then merely allowed to stand, slowly rusting away through the years. The rancher cannot afford to haul it all the miles back to town, for there is no profitable market for it as scrap-iron. The isolation of such a ranch is often depressing enough in itself. The depression must be doubled by the accumulation of junk. Thus, against the current of civilization, isolation and space may make a typically modern problem more acute for the far-off rancher than for the urbanite.

In city and country alike, the nation over, the century has seen possibly a thousandfold increase of junk, and at the same time the traditional agents of disposal have almost become extinct. If not quite vanished, like the passenger pigeon, they have become as rare as the whooping crane. The old-fashioned junkman has disappeared, and his bony horse with him. The small boy might still be happy to collect bottles, though even he is likely to be more profitably employed. In any case, most of the bottles are non-returnable. The housewife has no attic to serve as a first line of defense, and gets rid of larger objects only by haphazard means.

With junk, as with so much else in our civilization, we are approaching a crisis. We are producing junk enthusiastically, but we are just piling it up without getting rid of it. "Built-in obsolescence" carries this hidden price tag.

Consider merely one item—the television set. Produced by the collaboration of skilled scientists and skilled technologists, it may be considered almost the present end-point of our civilization. What becomes of the old one when you get a new one? Ask the dealer, and he will tell you that he merely throws it on the dump. Such sets are not as large as cars, and so we are not conscious of their being piled somewhere. Actually the situation is much worse. The car hulks are already routed for the making of new steel. The TV sets will not be used at all. They consist of glass, plastic, and various metals interlaced in such intricate fashion that they cannot be economically separated. We face, then, a melancholy thought. Except for those still in use and a few in museums or experimentally disassembled, every discarded TV set ever made now rests somewhere in a dump heap, and will so continue to rest, its materials being immortal, world-without-end.

In this modern world, strange stories circulate. One of them recently was of an urban family with three TV sets. Unusual affluence was not the cause; perhaps, rather, the reverse. This family frugally picked up its sets from discount houses or other stores where there was no trade-in for the old set. But what, eventually, is this family going to do? Will they pay someone to cart the old sets away? Or will they themselves take them to a dump? Or will they take them out and dump them by the side of the road somewhere, as some people abandon an old car?

Year by year, as cities grow and affluence continues, the piles of discarded materials grow higher. How long will it be (or has it already happened?) before our cities are like those isolated ranch houses, hemmed in and aesthetically oppressed by their own junk-heaps?

Of all the components of junk, as here considered, paper is the bulkiest and by far the greatest in weight, and even at the risk of a little repetition from an earlier chapter, its problem calls for further review. Paper is produced from wood, which comes from the cutting down of whole forests. Many of the paper companies have large holdings of forest land, and wood pulp is said to be insured for perpetuity. A vast and submerging flood of newsprint, wrappers, cartons, and toilet tissue will therefore continue to pour in upon us. Paper may be called the chief bulwark of our civilization. We can imagine civilization without steel or without gasoline. But we can scarcely imagine it without paper—everything from dollar bills and telephone directories to party hats and income-tax forms. Millions of dollars are expended annually to perfect the production and distribution of paper, and to stimulate the amount put to use. But how little money is expended upon getting rid of paper!

There are not, indeed, even any good figures to be cited. About a third of the whole is believed to be recycled, and to go into the production of new paper. A very small fraction is piled up for more or less permanent record, in public and private libraries and archives. The rest is returned, in one way or another, to the air, the water, or the land. Much of this huge remainder (figures are lacking) is burned, and thus passes chiefly into the atmosphere. A much smaller fraction—as toilet tissue, and in other forms—becomes water-borne, and eventually reaches the ocean. The rest (and it would seem to be a very large fraction) is thrown upon the land. Some of this, in individual sheets, becomes wet in the rain, and disintegrates. In larger masses, as in bundles of newspapers, paper is highly resistant to decay, and remains for many years.

One clear possibility toward alleviation would be the increase of the fraction of paper now recycled, though such a movement would meet with normal resistance from manufacturers of new paper. The chief difficulty is that used paper, per unit of weight, is of only minute value. In this connection there is a hierarchy of values, so that we can grade different kinds of waste paper all the way from patrician to plebeian. At the top, among recognized types, stand the old tabulator cards, commanding a price in the neighborhood of three cents a pound. Far lower come certain types of wrapping paper, at about half a cent. Newsprint is a little lower still, and at the very bottom, at about one-tenth of a cent, come magazines and cardboard cartons. "Slick" publications are thus ill-considered because their paper has been so heavily treated already that it is difficult to reclaim.

Even three cents a pound fails to constitute a product that can be carried far in search of a buyer. One-tenth of a cent a pound scarcely seems to be remuneration at all. Moreover, a curious kind of inverse law dominates the junk business, or what we might term the process of "counter-production." In ordinary merchandising everyone is adjusted to the idea of wholesale and retail prices. If you buy a small tablet, you expect the cost per sheet to be higher than if you buy a ream. A large business, purchasing half a million sheets at a time, gets an even lower price, and no one considers such a procedure discriminatory. But, in counter-production, as the used material starts back, the opposite law begins to work. The larger the amount, the higher the price per unit. If you collect a pound of used tabulator cards, you will be unable to find any one to give you three cents for them. In fact, those few cards will command no market at all. A hundred pounds of old newspapers (not a difficult amount to collect) should be worth almost 30¢. But try to sell them! In fact, most quotations on the junk market are for ton lots.

Apparently then, in such a material as waste paper, the value accrues from the process of collection. The material itself may be said to lack value altogether. In fact it often has even negative value, that is, the "owner" of it has to pay to have it taken away. A man with a six months' pile of newspaper thus does not possess an asset at all, but a liability, even though the waste-paper business in the country amounts to many millions of dollars yearly.

The situation, moreover, is not likely to change unless the whole economy declines sharply. As long as they are living well, people do not worry about failing to get a pittance for their old paper. They merely want to get rid of the nuisance of having it pile up. Most of them are even willing to pay moderately to have the stuff carted away.

A whole novel of modern life, indeed, might be written

about a neurotic man who became convinced that "they" were trying to get him by smothering him under paper. It comes pouring in, rising (in his tortured imagination) higher and higher. The postman's daily contribution becomes a terror. The newspaper, though he cannot live without it, dismays him, especially its Sunday issue. He cannot buy food without its being fearsomely polluted with wrappings and cartons. He cannot even, without apprehension, move his bowels. In desperation, trying to get rid of paper, he overuses the toilet and clogs it. The smog-control officers cite him for his smoky incinerator. Charitable organizations refuse to pick up his old newspapers. In the last chapter, when the decorator arrives with rolls of wallpaper, the poor fellow realizes that he is finally to be surrounded, breaks out screaming, and is taken away in a straitjacket.

Such an idle tale comes close to being sick humor if we realize that its anti-hero might stand as a symbol of civilization. His sense of suffocation, indeed, was psychological, not physical. So also it is with civilization. We are not actually going to be smothered by our heaps of paper and other waste materials, but we may become depressed by confusion and ugliness, and aesthetically deadened.

Paper is not only the chief single element in junk, but it is also largely typical. Its problem may therefore be even a little further explored.

As with so much else, the problem is twofold, involving collection, followed by disposal. As far as paper is concerned, neither functions well.

Better arrangements should certainly be worked out by municipalities so that the individual citizen could deliver his paper to depositories, which might serve the function of super-wastebaskets. The private automobile (until it is outlawed because of smog) would serve for a means of delivery. Such depositories might be financed out of tax money, but they would, eventually, be likely to operate on at least a break-even basis, since they could pass a large tonnage of material on to the dealers in paper. They would probably increase in an appreciable manner the fraction of paper that is being reprocessed.

But, as seems to be generally the case, the more difficult part of the problem is not collection, but disposal. Only a minute fraction of paper can be floated away in the streams. Paper burns readily, but thus increases the smog problem. Paper on the land remains indefinitely.

The fact is that paper is an unnatural substance. It is essentially cellulose, as is wood. But it is cellulose so treated as to be even slower to return to the soil than wood itself. Bacteria and other agents of decay are ready at hand to attack such natural and ancient materials as sewage and garbage. But no bacteria have as yet had time to evolve with a taste for such a sophisticated material as paper. Our papermakers have done too well, and have learned to make too durable a product. Perhaps the bacteriologists can rush to our rescue, by discovering or developing a paper-ravenous organism. Perhaps the papermakers themselves can discover, not merely a built-in obsolescence, but actually a built-in disintegration.

Even books, which might be considered the highest manifestation of paper, are beginning to be an embarrassment. They are extraordinarily durable. "Book-burning" is a term of anathema. But did you ever try to burn a book? Anyone who does so try might well be considered, in the words of the old song, more to be pitied than censured. Actually, in the large-scale process of counter-production, books are not burned but are shredded and re-pulped, as happens with many thousands of unsold paperbacks every month.

Even the piling-up of books in libraries carries the threat of stifling civilization with the dead hand of the past, and—mechanically, and in a mere areal sense—of making libraries as large as towns. The rising curve of acquisitions in any large library is frightening.

As in most of these situations, the ancients had it better. Their papyrus went to pieces in less than a hundred years. Unless someone took the trouble to copy a whole book onto new papyrus, that work vanished—and in most instances, certainly, a good riddance. There, also, goes the story of the "destruction" of the great Alexandrian library. No one needed to destroy it. Just leave it alone for a hundred years, and it is gone! But we are preserving, for future generations, many millions of comic strips and daily stock quotations. . . .

The different constituents of junk need not be considered separately. Scrap metal, tin cans, rags, glass, plastics, rubber, feathers, hair—each presents much the same problem as does paper. They may be said to display a general hierarchy, ranging from the expensive metals to the old tires, which command no market at all, create a horrible smoke, and are practically immune to decay.

All the chief junk materials display the inverse law of

value, being priced usually in ton lots. There is little motivation, therefore, for their collection at the household level. All the materials are slow to mingle with the soil, and some of them, notably glass and plastics, retain their integrity, humanly speaking, forever. . . .

Fixated as few nations have ever been upon the idea of production—its nobility and essential greatness—the American people have been, and remain, peculiarly unfitted to deal with the problem of junk. The farmer, the miner, the manufacturer—these are our heroes, the giants of production. Whoever awarded a medal or an honorary degree to a junkman? We should be erecting monuments to him! Actually, we are doing just the opposite, making it more difficult for him to earn a living. "Up-to-date" zoning regulations have forced junk-dealers out of their locations, and even made it difficult for them to relocate. The actual number of collectors has decreased.

The reason given for such restrictions is that junkyards are "unaesthetic." One wonders just how much less aesthetic they may be than the unsightly collection of "slurb" in which they are usually ensconced. Any junkyard, moreover, can be pretty well hidden behind a board fence. Again, as with the antipathy to heaps of automobile hulks, one senses a deeper psychological feeling. When it comes to despoiling an alpine valley with a lumber mill or a power plant the public is generally quite reconciled to aesthetic deprivation. Such aesthetic blights have to do with production. . . .

With junk, as with other phases of the disposal problem, the ideal is to work toward recycling. In certain areas the situation has already advanced considerably.

Without the recycling of metal scrap, indeed, our industries would already be suffering shortages. The recovery of copper equals 80 per cent of newly-mined domestic copper. Recovery of lead is the equivalent of 200 per cent of the production of the mines of the United States. In fact, most of the nonferrous metals present only a minor disposal problem.

That problem builds up with iron and steel, paper and glass, and with all kinds of fabricated materials—not only the TV sets and old automobiles that have been already mentioned, but also washing machines and all sort of "appliances," rubber tires, bicycles and children's toys, broken crockery and dishes, and the other almost infinite paraphernalia of modern civilization.

Recycling, on a basis of profit, is not going to solve the problem. As always, it can be repeated, the situation is not going to solve itself, and any solution is going to cost money.

Since an active Secondary Materials business is already in operation, the best means of improving the situation would seem to be cooperation and stimulation. Instead of being harassed by zoning laws, the junk-dealers should be encouraged or even in certain ways subsidized. Municipal paper-depositories could work harmoniously with the dealers, and might even be established in conjunction with the yards.

Depositories for old appliances should also receive public aid. Such items, once collected in numbers, would probably become subject to the price tendencies of "counter-production," and thus assume value. At the very least, instead of being piled into vaster and vaster dumps, such devices, being heavier than water and biologically inert, might receive decent burial at sea, or even in the deeper lakes.

Still another approach to the problem of junk is possible, and it is perhaps most striking when applied to the automobile. This we may call actual design for recycling. In our essentially unplanned economy any such practice may prove to be impracticable, but it at least possesses some basis in logic.

Just as wrapping paper and newsprint might be made more palatable to bacteria, so our appliances, and even the automobile itself, might be planned with some consideration for eventual recycling.

Aside from a certain amount of plastic, rubber, and other organic materials, the automobile consists of metals, chiefly of iron and steel. Mingled with these, however, are certain other metals, some of which interfere with the recycling—copper in the wiring, and in the brass fittings, such as the radiator; zinc also in the brass fittings, and in such castings as the door-handles; aluminum in the pistons and elsewhere; lead, chiefly in the battery. Other metals are present in small quantities—such as the chromium, which makes a great display of itself but exists in such a thin coating of plate as to amount to little in actual weight. So also the amounts of the other metals, such as nickel and tin, are negligible. Really to be considered, therefore, aside from the dominating iron and steel, are lead, zinc, copper, and aluminum.

The lead is concentrated in the battery, where it is easily separable. It is of sufficient value to be worth the separation, and so causes no problem of recycling. So also it is with aluminum, which is volatilized in the furnaces. Though it is lost, it at least does no harm.

Zinc and copper cause the trouble—the former by damaging the furnace linings, and the latter by merely staying put and deteriorating the steel into which it is finally incorporated.

A possibility would therefore seem to be to design a car without zinc or copper. Door-handles, for instance, might be of plastic or of aluminum. Some metal other than copper could serve for wiring.

On the other hand, since the automobile itself—or, at least, the internal-combustion engine—will apparently have to be given up because of its production of poisonous smog, its redesign in its few remaining years may be considered an unnecessary labor.

Even at this eleventh hour, however, one palliative should certainly be a law aimed against the abandonment of old cars. Such a law would not affect the cars piling up in those great heaps, for they are already channeled for the melting furnaces. It would affect, instead, the cars left on small-town dumps or merely abandoned beside the road or on a city street. One possibility would be to require a certification as to the disposal of a car already licensed before a new license could be issued. Or the tax and licensing charge against a car could be continued until it had been properly written off. Since the state recognizes the existence of an automobile by licensing and taxing it, the state may also, with no great or difficult extension of authority, take cognizance of the final disposal. . . .

This chapter has thus returned to its point of beginning—the automobile hulk. The suggestion has been made that some deeper psychological feeling affects the American's attitude in this respect, so that his reaction leads him to some such word as "Shocking!"

The reason would seem to be that the abandoned car brings to him an image of death. His car, to the average man, has even been called a sex symbol. Certainly he is deeply identified with it. In that heap of dead cars, he sees, unconsciously, a heap of corpses. He even views himself—old, impotent, dead. He sees the end-point. Having, probably, no great or immediate confidence in his own immortality, he does not remember that these old cars will go to the furnaces, and return again as shining new cars.

Without some such explanation, we can hardly understand the situation, that people are so concerned about these piles of inert steel.

8

LITTER

"Monkeys cannot be housebroken"

LITTER DOES NOT PRESENT the most pressing of disposal problems, but it may well be the most difficult to solve. Not creating a serious hazard to public health, it escapes the concentrated bombardment from the heavy artillery of Public Health services. It is highly irritating, but its abolition is scarcely imperative. Only in the long pull can it become critical for civilization, if it should drag down the collective sense of decency and order, without which a society cannot, indefinitely, function in healthy fashion.

The problem is so difficult because it springs from the limitations of the individual human being. In a given case and at a particular moment, the ordinary person finds that to drop something or to throw it away is easier than to give it proper disposal. Again, and without too much flight of fancy, we are back at the psychology of the arboreal creature—let it drop, and it disappears forever. Monkeys cannot be housebroken. . . .

The word "litter" came into the language with the Norman Conquest, its connection with the French *lit,* (bed) being clear. Here, indeed, we have an exception to the general rule (as many will remember from the opening pages of Scott's *Ivanhoe*) that Norman words served for articles of luxury and Anglo-Saxon words were useful in the kitchen and the stable. Just why the Anglo-Saxon *bed* triumphed over *lit* may be because *litter*, from the beginning, seems to have had barnyard associations. It meant, apparently, not the Norman lord's bed, but the Norman lord's horse's bed, the straw that was spread about in the stall. Since many Saxon serfs slept in much the same manner, or worse, litter came to mean an improvised bed of straw, and so may have eventually given rise to the Americanism, "hit the hay." It also came to mean an improvised bed for carrying sick or wounded persons, but soon passed on to denote, not a place of repose, but the mere scattering of straw, hay and any kind of miscellaneous material.

As a specific American "problem," litter scarcely obtained recognition before the lavish nineteen-twenties. Since Depression is a natural antidote, the problem did not become acute in the thirties, and even the war of the nineteen-forties worked against it in the home country, no matter how much litter the hostilities created in countries that suffered bombing and fighting. The sudden surge occurred in the postwar years of ever-increasing production of consumer goods and general luxury. The term *litter* then came into general use; soon afterward, *litterbug*—triumphant as a word, though hopelessly futile in combating the practice at which it was aimed. In 1953 Keep America Beautiful was organized, chiefly as an anti-litter association.

This organization, generally known as KAB, has both worked for the elimination of litter and collected information. By public opinion polls it seems to have determined that men are worse litterers than are women, that local residents cause more litter than do tourists, and that not much less litter is deposited in winter than in summer.

KAB has also compiled some figures. The total yearly cost to the taxpayer for the removal of litter, urban and rural, is a half-billion dollars. If the litter thrown yearly upon and along all highways were to be concentrated upon one highway, it would cover such a road, from New York to San Francisco, a foot deep.

Litter may be roughly defined—at least, for present purposes—as what is thrown away upon public property. In certain usages of the word, it is extended to include general mess on private property, as in backyards and even inside buildings, especially in basements and attics. Such accumulations are especially dangerous as creating a fire hazard, and in extreme cases they may constitute a public menace. But they present a different problem from the one here considered.

So also, the scattering of material in semipublic places may be largely passed over. Before a baseball game the stands are sufficiently neat and clean. At the end of the ninth inning they are strewn—one can almost say "deep"— with paper cups, discarded scorecards, newspapers, bottles, cans, paper bags and containers, cigarette butts and cigar butts, the melted ice-cream of accidentally-dropped cones, peanut shells, and a thousand other such things, filthy or otherwise. Yet the situation does not create a litter problem. Each person has paid for his seat, and he has bought from a vendor most of the material that he has later thrown away. So also, he has paid for its removal. After the game, the cleaners move in, and put the stands to rights for the next game. It is all a private, self-contained action, with the cost of clean-up necessarily written into the economics of the operation.

The crowding of baseball stands being what it is, there is scarcely any way in which disposal cans or waste baskets can be provided. The bad feature, however, is that the system breeds carelessness. The baseball fan goes on to spread his litter carelessly along the highway or at a picnic spot, where he has not paid for the cost of clean-up afterward.

Many other such public-private situations cause trouble. One of them is the drive-in. Such places regularly provide litter cans, but many patrons go on the assumption that the price of the food and drink includes clean-up afterward—and, indeed, they must be basically right. So they drop their leavings out of the car window. Again, the system breeds carelessness. But more, cleanup of such premises probably comes but once a day, and in the meantime the public has suffered the mess. Moreover, before clean-up time comes, the winds may have blown paper napkins and paper cups a long distance, and deposited them upon other private premises, or upon public property. . . .

The causes of the litter problem are not hard to state. Given arboreal habits and the normal trait of doing something in the easiest immediate way, and on top of these create a heavy population, living in what is, historically speaking, an incredible affluence—and we have litter. Recently, indeed, there has even been the suggestion that

Affluent Society is an outmoded term. Now, should it not be the Throw-away Society?

As a personal reminiscence of the tie between litter and affluence, the author remembers Mexico of the nineteen-thirties. It was a place where, at any eating of lunch in the open, one was likely to be surrounded, at respectful distance, by small boys, curious and observant. They were not, I think, actually hungry, except as all small boys are likely to be hungry. After eating, one could merely go off, knowing that the boys were only too happy to move in and clean up. They ate what food was left. They salvaged wrapping papers and cartons. They seized upon tin cans as treasure trove.

The specific cure for litter, therefore, might be a severe depression. Such a cure, however, would certainly be worse than the disease.

Without too much beating of breast and crying of *"Mea culpa!"* one may even believe that the traditions of the American people have made them peculiarly susceptible to the disease of littering. The United States developed from a frontier society. The frontier cultivated some virtues, but neatness was not one of them. By all accounts, a newly-founded settlement soon became dirty and unkempt. Even yet, in such regions as Alaska, one notes the same tendency. In fact, people in the far north seem merely to count upon the snow covering everything for half of the year anyway.

A large proportion of Americans, moreover, spring from a background of the slum, where their grandparents or great-grandparents lived as newly-arrived immigrants. Like the frontier, the slum provided no training in neatness.

As compared with certain peoples, beyond doubt, the Americans are nothing better than slovenly. Public campgrounds in Norway or Sweden, for instance, seem immaculate in comparison with those in our national forests. . . .

The problem of litter is both rural and urban. It began in connection with human habitation, and continued with the custom, in medieval cities and even in later ones, of throwing all unwanted objects into the streets. Regulation gradually opposed such practices, and much of what was originally urban litter became sewage and garbage. But modern cities still had to accept responsibility for street-cleaning, and the street-sweepers, or so-called "whitewings," waged an endless and drawn battle with miscellaneous waste—and more particularly with horse-droppings—clear down into the opening decade of the twentieth century. As long as the horse provided the chief problem, there could scarcely be much concern about the individual citizen's contributions, such as cigar butts, chewing gum and its wrappers, and other oddments, especially of paper.

With the horse gone, but with affluence ever increasing, the situation failed to show the improvement that might have been expected. About the only notable advance was that the American city-dwellers did not, as the horses had done, use the streets for defecatory purposes, though the notorious lack of public urinals still forced the males at least to some employment of walls in the Biblical manner. In fact, growing affluence, increased concentration of people (and of dogs), and continuing simian carelessness seemed to offset any gain effected by the exit of the horse.

Along with that noble but messy animal, the whitewings too seem to have vanished, and the cities, with typical American reliance upon power-machines, have introduced mechanical sweepers. Even if these devices kept ahead of the litter-makers on the streets (and they seldom did), the sidewalks remained a private matter. As a desperate remedy municipalities then actually appealed to the better nature of the citizens, installing litter cans on street corners and praying the citizens to be helpful. The appeal worked well enough to fill many litter cans, but not well enough to make much difference in the untidiness and even nastiness of the streets and sidewalks, especially in the more crowded and poorer districts.

The situation as regards urban litter thus stands. It may be considered an extension of the garbage problem. It can be kept under control by more tax money spent for street-cleaning, by regulations requiring property owners to sweep their sidewalks, by more litter cans, and by the education of public opinion. . . .

The real crisis is with non-urban litter, and most people, in fact, thus think of the term primarily. As non-urban must be included the environs of cities, and the larger parks. Primarily, this type of litter collects and concentrates along routes of travel (whether motor roads or foot trails or rivers) and in what could once be called "God's out-of-doors." Litter-makers are especially addicted to campgrounds, fishing spots, and scenic viewpoints.

Particularly tempting to the throw-away-prone individual is any kind of water surface. If you toss a tin can into a pool, it makes a fine splash. Then it either sinks, or floats downstream in a rather amusing way. Soon it goes down, to foul the stream-bottom, disturb the life cycle, and create unsightliness, as seen through clear water.

The tendency, though a stronger word is needed, of the litter-maker to defile and befoul the most beautiful natural spots almost passes the limits of ordinary probability. Some people seem to take a particular delight, unconscious perhaps, in strewing their own offal about in such places. Where old U.S. 40 crosses Donner Pass, the state of California has provided a parking space and lookout. The view eastward, down the granite slopes and across the blue lake, has always been one of exceptional beauty. It still is, if one keeps the eyes high. Just over the railing and a few feet down, lies a garbage dump. Though a litter can is nearby, our average American citizens have not bothered to use it, but have merely dropped whatever they happened to have left over. Flies buzz over the mess, and rodents forage in it. Probably no health hazard thus arises, but such a sight tends to breed feelings of disgust and even of hatred for the dirty human race.

As usual, gross estimates result in such large figures as to become meaningless. KAB has calculated that the materials jettisoned on or along the roads in one year amount to a bulk of 18 million cubic yards. The highways have thus become beautifully engineered strips of concrete, edged on both sides by continuous low mounds of garbage-like litter. Park at some spot on a highway, and then walk along the shoulder!

One man has done some counting on his own. Some years ago, near a small industrial city in Virginia, he found 7,000 tin cans per mile over a stretch of ten miles. Fifty miles out of San Francisco, in a region of much natural beauty, he estimated, for a single mile, 20,000 cans. If someone should go to the trouble of carefully laying these cans end-to-end, the approximate result would be a continuous snaking line of cans on each side of the pavement.

Both of these counts were made when the highways were only a few years old. Since no one is likely to have removed any cans, the number has probably doubled, or more, since that time.

Litter along highways, moreover, exists far-off from

cities. Some years ago the author had occasion to cross Arizona and New Mexico by U.S. 66 in company with a geologist, who stopped every few miles to look at outcrops, and left his companion with the car. Strolling along the highway-shoulder, even in that almost uninhabited country, the author found both sides of the highway to be filthy with the debris thrown from passing cars, most of which had probably been traveling at high speed.

As the mentions of highways indicate, the problem of nonurban litter is especially associated with the automobile. A good guess would be that 95 per cent of such litter was either thrown from a car or thus carried to its immediate place of disposal. The car gives both mobility and irresponsibility. Refuse can be dropped with impunity, and then left behind.

The whole tradition of the automobile, unfortunately, has fostered such procedure. One may even, to some extent, blame the manufacturers. Just as they have considered safety to be a dirty word, so they have constructed cars on the assumption that refuse is merely to be, in carefree fashion, tossed out. Even the ashtray, as a standard fixture, appeared late, and was motivated by the idea of fire prevention, not of cleanliness. The ashtray itself is merely a halfway step, and one often sees, within a few feet of the disposal can, the pile of butts dumped on the ground. Even now, any kind of waste-basket for a car must be purchased as an extra, and crowded into a place where no space has been provided.

While billions of dollars have been spent in advertising cars, have these advertisers spent any dollars at all in educating people not to throw trash out of car windows?

(Yet even here the winds of change are blowing. While the book is in proof, a brewing corporation runs a full-page advertisement in a national magazine, urging people against creating litter with empty beer cans, bottles, and watermelon rinds. Perhaps we have here a sign for the future.)

Just as 95 per cent of rural litter may be directly credited to automobiles, so also at least 90 per cent of it consists of a few materials. Poured-out liquids sink into the ground or run into the streams, and thrown-away food quickly rots or supplies forage for scavenging rodents. "The pill" has largely removed one of the classic items of litter. Nearly all of it now consists of paper, butts, cans, and glass.

The paper appears chiefly in the form of containers for food and drink—cartons, beer packs and soft-drink packs, wrappings of all sorts. Much of this material is cardboard or heavy waxed paper—both highly durable. Like so much else, all this is not just going to go away on its own.

Butts, to some extent, are paper, and traditionally they were altogether paper and tobacco. That good old-fashioned butt offered little difficulty. The thin paper disintegrated in the rain, and the shredded tobacco went back into the soil as leaf-mold. But, as in so much else, modern technology has produced a litter problem. With the general tendency of our civilization to neglect disposal, the technologists have created almost immortal butts, which are rapidly forming a kind of carpet at all roadside stops, and an ever-increasing scatter over the beaches.

As for metal cans, the United States produces, in a single year, 48 billion of them, and an appreciable percentage of them get thrown from car windows or dropped at picnicking tables. The formula seems to be, "Park, drink, throw the can out!" Beer cans are the most numerous along the roadside, but soft-drink cans run a good second. In campgrounds and luncheon-spots the cans of macaroni, baked beans, and corned beef supply a large proportion.

As with cigarette butts, modern ingenuity has exacerbated the situation. The old-fashioned tin can disintegrated in time. Slowly indeed, but in the course of ten years or so, the paper wrapping and the lacquer deteriorated, the tin-plating cracked, the steel rusted, and the earth received its own. Then, as if not content that even time should destroy, the technicians produced the aluminum can. In human terms, aluminum is everlasting. Under most conditions the discarded aluminum can may laugh at the centuries.

Ingenuity, in the name of convenience, also contrived the so-called self-opening can. This little invention merely doubled the disposal problem by creating two pieces, instead of one, to be individually picked up or thrown into the litter can. Moreover, the torn-off tab is sharp-edged, and can be dangerous, especially to small children.

As may be expected in our civilization, the aluminum can and the self-opening can have been marketed in the name of convenience, with no regard to disposal. Moreover, the millions of dollars spent in advertising to introduce the new devices have, apparently, not included a nickel toward educating people about disposal. A recent

TV commercial, for instance, showed a number of jolly fellows having a splendid time drinking their beer at a picnic. As each man ripped off the self-opener, what did he do with it? Naturally, he threw it on the ground.

As lavish with glass as with tin and aluminum, the United States produces yearly 26 billion bottles and jars, about 135 for each person. If you are an average citizen, you must dispose of two or three bottles a week. People in higher income brackets have to dispose of half a dozen. In addition, each of these containers must have a cover or stopper, so that the disposal problem is vastly complicated.

Like aluminum, glass may be considered immortal. In the milling action of a shingle beach, it is gradually ground into inoffensive pebble-like morsels. Elsewhere it simply remains. It often so remains in the jagged and knife-like fragments so characteristic of whiskey bottles thrown from car windows.

Many bottles are now of plastic, but we can thus gain little comfort. Unless exposed to a very hot fire, this plastic is as immortal as glass, and will not even so easily grind to pieces under the action of pebbles and sea waves.

On the whole, however, bottles are a less formidable component of litter than are tin cans. This may be merely because few people drink as many bottles of bourbon as they do cans of beer. Moreover, a larger proportion of the billions of bottles and jars is consumed in the kitchen and the bathroom, and so is committed to the garbage can. Some have also suggested that there is an old American folkway against reckless smashing of bottles. This seems doubtful, and in any case a man who has just emptied a bottle of whiskey is likely to suffer a breakdown of restraints.

The chief villains of the piece are thus four—paper, butts, cans, glass. In the wings stands plastic, waiting. What can be done about it? . . .

Litter having attained the status of a public problem only within the last two decades, there exists no traditional approach to its alleviation, and the result has been a kind of fumbling scramble. People began saying, "There ought to be a law!" and in short order there was not only a law, but a separate and different law for every state. By the passage of such laws a slight easing of guilt may have been effected, but not much else.

By the very nature of its origin, littering is not directly

controllable by laws. It originates from millions of people, at millions of points. These people are not criminals and are not criminally-minded even when they are breaking the anti-litter laws. Granted, they may not constitute the most cultured and highly-responsible segment of the population. Even so, they may well constitute three-quarters of the whole.

Moreover, the laws are obviously unenforceable. Policemen have other things to do than to hide in the bushes to waylay someone who throws a beer can out of his car window. In 1965 the thirty-five states that then maintained separate records on litter violations reported a total of 9,488 arrests. That figure is unimpressive and negligible in comparison with the millions of litterers, and the billions of individual items of litter.

These scarcely more than occasional arrests may, indeed, accomplish more harm than good. To make an example of a man may only turn him vindictive, and the chance of littering with impunity is so overwhelming that the possibility of encountering the law a second time can hardly serve as a deterrent. There is even the hazard of the malicious litterbug, such as the one who was recently reported as strewing New York streets with scraps of paper.

The signs "$100 FINE" look horrendous, but that is about all. Probably they have a little educational value, and perhaps the generation of children growing up under their influence may be thus swayed, more than by the present example of their parents. Also in the direction of education for children and childlike adults are the "cute" signs of animals with brooms, in the tradition of Smokey the Bear, the great triumph of the Forest Service; Maryland has "Sweepy the Squirrel," and Kansas has "Parky the Kangaroo." Other states have invented human anti-litterbugs, according to local traditions—"Daniel Broom" for Kentucky, and "Colonel Clean" for Mississippi. Keep America Beautiful reports that these animals are performing a noble service. "Noble," we may grant; "effective," we may doubt. Still, the effort deserves support, as a good try, in the best traditions of American advertising.

Certainly, the providing of waste-disposal cans along the highways and at stopping points has been useful. The thirty-six states that reported to KAB in 1965 had placed 38,000 such disposal units, with Virginia leading at 5,000, and Michigan a close second.

Not only are cans now almost universal at campgrounds and picnicking spots, but many states also provide them at rest areas and viewpoints along highways. Some people use them conscientiously, but many other people, unfortunately, do not, and dump their leavings on the ground, happily, within a few feet of the can. Moreover, the existence of cans, at best, merely turns the problem from one of litter to one of garbage. The contents have to be collected and dumped, and in rush times sufficient money is not always available. The overflowed can is a common sight, and the picnicker who then adds his contribution to the overflow-pile can scarcely even be accused of breaking a law. Like the "cute" animals, the litter cans accomplish something, but cannot provide a solution.

In fact, as with all situations involving the folkways of millions of people, there is scarcely a possibility of anything so simple as to be called a solution. There can only be alleviations here and there, and gradual improvement.

Certain palliatives, not yet much in use, may be suggested. The law, it would seem, might be more effectively directed, not at the individual litterbug, but at the wholesale producer of unnecessary litter, that is, at the manufacturer.

The requirement of a properly-designed and installed trash basket in every automobile would be helpful and reasonable. Most service stations now have some kind of barrel or oil-drum where rubbish can be dumped; the maintenance of such a can, plainly labeled as for public use, should be obligatory. Such legal attacks upon the problem can be justified, not only upon the perhaps uncertain ground of aesthetics, but upon safety. Blowing papers are a threat, and some kinds of litter can cause skids; in forested areas the paper creates a fire hazard.

The aluminum can should be flatly outlawed. There seems to be no possible excuse for it. It could probably be taxed out of existence. Such a move would meet bitter resistance from the aluminum companies, but then it might win equally strong support from the steel and tin-plate manufacturers.

The "self-opening" can should either be outlawed or remodeled. Probably a can could be designed so that the knife-like tab could merely be pulled back, but would remain attached to the can.

Bottles might well be legally standardized as to sizes and shapes, so that they could be recycled more economically. As it is, a bottle for Product X has to be returned so that it can be refilled with that same product, and the process is highly inefficient. Possibly our lives might lose a little glamor by the disappearance of certain well-known and individual glass-shapes. On the other hand, if manufacturers specialized less on the bottle and more on its contents, we might benefit.

For a comparison, take the French wine industry. It is more glamorous and individualistic than anything this country is likely to produce, but it operates on an absolute minimum of variety of bottles. Except for Champagne and Alsace, all France gets along on two shapes, two colors, and one standard size. Bottles scarcely occur as litter in France. Even those left by American tourists are soon picked up and recirculated. Partly this is the result of traditional Gallic frugality, but re-use is made easy by standardization—much to the regret, indeed, of local bottle-makers.

On the contrary, in the United States the re-use of certain bottles is actually illegal, and they are so marked. Our law therefore requires that we should make the disposal problem harder.

Even as it is, many bottles have a sufficient re-market value to be collected and sold. Affluence may be a national trait, but it does not prevent the ordinary housewife from feeling non-affluent toward the end of the weekly or monthly pay check. Typically, she returns to the supermarket all the bottles that are returnable. There is even a marginal industry of bottle-collecting. Readers of Truman Capote's *In Cold Blood* can remember the episode in which the murderers aided two hitchhikers at picking bottles from the roadside, and with results that, in most countries, would have meant high wages.

The return of bottles even shows in the statistics. The country produces only (if the word is applicable) 26 billion bottles and jars yearly, but it produced for them 65 billion metal and plastic caps and crowns. Unless we have a high export of caps and crowns, these figures indicate that the average bottle is used five times in two years.

Still, affluence affects the situation. A recent estimate is that, in the Detroit area alone, bottles with a *deposit-return value* were lying around to the total value of $841,000. Many of these bottles were cluttering basements and storage closets, but many of them also were lying as litter. Since the total number of bottles was given as 24 million, the average value must have been taken at about four cents.

On the whole, it would seem that the problem of the bottle, in litter and otherwise, might be solved at the economic level, with the help of some well-constructed legislation. . . .

Another approach to the litter problem has been by direct clean-up, whether by amateur enthusiasts or by tax-supported collectors. Various organizations have made litter-retrieval an activity—for instance the Boy Scouts, the Girl Scouts, the Camp Fire Girls, the YWCA, the YMCA. The Sierra Club, in 1958, picked an estimated 26,000 cans out of a small area of the high country. Some states and many cities maintain a more less effective professional pick-up of litter.

Although such measures may be necessary in the present emergency, they seem basically wrong. Why should our great civilization expect the decent people to go around picking up the mess left by the slatterns? Or why should we tax the decent people for the same end? Moreover, the collection of litter is too expensive for the results attained.

The state of Illinois, for 1965, paid for the retrieval of litter the sum of almost three million dollars. During the spring clean-up in the Chicago area, 360 men were engaged in the work, and they employed "100 dump trucks, 29 street-sweepers, 12 front-end loaders, a forced-water tank truck, and a machine called a scavenger-inductor (an oversized vacuum cleaner)."

An estimated fifty million dollars is expended yearly to remove litter from only the so-called "primary highways." Even so, the highways are not clean, and often are filthy.

Even more discouraging is the cost of retrieval per item. Out of the window goes an empty cigarette pack, a beer can, or a coke bottle. The bottle, returned, may be worth a few cents; the other items are valueless. Yet Nevada estimates that the cost of the collection of *one* item from the highway is *ten cents*. Many other estimates have run much higher.

We have here a kind of final *reductio ad absurdum*. Our people throw worthless objects away, and then, through taxes, pay fantastic amounts to have the worthless objects picked up.

Even so, there is no appreciable gain. As a letter from the Nevada Department of Highways concludes plaintively, "Sorry to say we aren't able to observe much in the way of favorable results."

Tax money, one would think, might be much more profitably spent in stimulating or even subsidizing the process of recycling. During the Second World War our housewives flattened their tin cans, and put them out for collection. Housewives could do so again, a slight premium being offered—perhaps trading-stamps or a bingo prize. The tons of cans thus collected would be kept out of the garbage and also out of the litter. In the end, the total operation would doubtless be much cheaper. . . .

As the years pass, education will probably be the best recourse. We may even gather a little hope from the recent experience of such a state as Wisconsin, where a vigorous campaign of education has been in action for some years. Though litter, over the country generally, was increasing in 1965, Wisconsin was able to report a modest improvement.

Children must be taught young, in schools or elsewhere, that they no longer live in a frontier society of much country and few people. They must absorb deeply the idea that civilization and the good life, and the escape from the slum, depend upon picking up behind oneself. This will be no easy lesson to be mastered by a basically arboreal species, and the process has hardly begun. We can look forward to a generation or two of living with the filth along highways, in picnicking and camping spots, and at scenic lookouts. In all likelihood, as population and affluence increase, the mess is going to get worse, as the outdoors itself degenerates toward a slum. The effect upon the national psychology of thus living in the litter is likely to be depressive.

9

AGRICULTURAL REFUSE

The Augean Stables

As THE GREEKS told the tale, King Augeas of Elis owned three thousand oxen. In the curious and dreamlike manner of mythological stories, the tellers assigned no motive for his keeping these beasts as he did. Instead of letting them range around in pastures, as would have been expected, he penned them in a stable. Moreover, he did not have his slaves clean the pens and spread the manure on the fields. Thirty years passed, and as a result, naturally, the accumulation became appalling. As one of his twelve labors, Heracles was assigned the task of cleaning the stables, and he did so in one day, as the story goes, by turning the course of the Alpheus River to run through the stables and wash them out.

The tale induces some speculations. Had the pre-classical Greeks not yet grasped the idea of fertilizing their fields, so that manure was considered merely a waste product? What was the condition of the Alpheus River afterward?

The tale also has its implications for the present. Many places in the United States are rapidly coming to rival the Augean Stables, and many rivers are thus being forced to do the work once assigned to the Alpheus. . . .

The complex and enormous problem of agricultural refuse is serious, even if compared with such gigantic ones as that of human sewage. In mere bulk and tonnage it is so great as almost to preclude calculation. Moreover, agricultural waste is involved with active poisons. At the risk of over-simplification, we may merely put it that the whole problem presents three chief phases—field-refuse, pesticides, and manure.

Field-refuse includes straw, chaff, hulls, vegetable tops, cuttings and prunings, and all other such leftovers to the total of many millions of tons annually. Since forestry is now generally included as part of agriculture, here also must be included the leftovers of the lumbering industry, those mountains of slash, sawdust, and trimmings.

Nonetheless, in spite of its bulk, field-refuse creates little present problem. It is traditional, and has, so to speak, always existed. There are well-established methods by which it is handled, and it has been written into the expense, time, and labor of year-to-year operation. In addition, field agriculture necessarily enjoys space. By long custom, the wanted and unwanted parts of the crop are largely separated in the field. There is not, and scarcely can be, an "urbanization" of agriculture.

Much of the refuse is plowed under, and helps to maintain the fertility of the soil. Most of the rest is burned, and thus committed to the atmosphere. In the long run, such combustion creates air pollution, but space, once more, prevents the acute difficulties that have arisen in cities. Agricultural refuse is burned, in any particular place, only during a few days of the year, and generally does not do more than create a temporary and local smoke problem.

Indeed there is something almost satisfying about agricultural burning. The tall columns of smoke which lean off with the wind, the just pleasantly acrid smell, both seem to be a part of the poetry, over the centuries, associated with an autumn day. There may be abuses, and one of them is certainly the unnecessary pall of smoke that many lumber mills keep sending out to smudge the clean mountain air. More efficient burners could certainly be developed. Even so, man's adjustment to clean woodsmoke is an ancient one, and he can be comfortable with it. The smoke of lumber mills is far different from the black belch of unrestrained factory chimneys and from the crawling yellow smog of cities. . . .

Pesticides—at least, as of the year 1962—seem to be almost the personal property of the late Rachel Carson. Her *Silent Spring* presented the problem vividly, was read by millions of people, and had much effect. Her high indignation carried the implication that many users of pesticides were, in some way, vicious people.

If common practice could have kept up with common sense Miss Carson would really have been belaboring a dead horse. Even when her book appeared, the whole approach to agricultural pests—whether insects, worms, fungi, or weeds—was rapidly changing into something else by new scientific discoveries.

As for the implication that the users of pesticides were vicious people, basically antisocial, one may admit that a few of them were, and are. Here one would be likely to include some of the producers and salesmen of pesticides who still plaster the billboards with advertisements to hit the bugs with their stronger chemicals, apparently with no consideration of long-range effects. On the whole, however, as in most social complexes, the vicious are not nearly so important a component as the merely ignorant, along with those who are simply self-seeking in an ordinarily human manner.

In fact, the philosophy of the pesticide-user is a simple and ordinary one, such as any person can understand. If a gnat or fly settles on your bare hand and starts to bite, you slap it with your other hand. The reaction is so simple as to be almost a reflex. In killing the gnat or fly, you cannot stop to consider the ultimate and possibly the far-reaching effects on the whole biological ecology. Having squashed the pest, you may very well, then, ask the question, "Have I, in this action, disturbed the whole balance of nature?"

The farmer is in an analogous situation. The insects attack his crop, and he in turn, altogether naturally, delivers a super-slap. Certainly the farmer was scarcely to be blamed in those years following the Second World War, when he was being urged on by agricultural experts and by manufacturers, all gone wild with the glamor of newly developed chemicals.

In their history, the pesticides scarcely antedate the nineteen-forties. Traditionally, throughout the long centuries of agriculture, there was no such thing. God sent the locusts that ate the wheat, and then came a starving time. So also God sent the mysterious and equally devastating blights and cankers, though no one could see by what means the blights and cankers worked their evil. Sometimes, too, God could be credited with relief, as when the seagulls came and fell upon the crickets that were devouring Mormon crops by the Great Salt Lake. As in other matters, whichever way it went, all one could say was, "Blessed be the name of the Lord!"

Man got along. Sometimes, unknown to him, the mere process of evolution helped him. Necessarily, he used the seed of plants that had survived the plague, and thus developed resistant strains. Sometimes luck was with him. In the medieval manor, crops were planted in long narrow strips, not in broad fields. Such a pattern must have done something to slow down the spread of insects, though never designed for that purpose.

In most departments of human endeavor, empirical usage precedes scientific knowledge. With pesticides the contrary seems to have been true. Only in the later nineteenth century, with the accumulation of chemical and biological data, did the general use of pesticides begin. The first ones consisted of metallic compounds, especially of arsenic, copper, and lead. They were known to be poisons, and the chief danger associated with their use was thought to be their accidental intake by children. A few children must die. No one, however, seems to have been much concerned about what effect the accumulation of such poisons might have upon the soil. Such bad effects could appear in two ways. First, the soil itself could be poisoned so that it could no longer produce crops. Second, the crops could pick up the poisons from the soil, and pass these along to human consumers.

Not by foresight, but by mere good luck (and where, indeed, would the human race be without plentiful good luck?), neither of these possibilities has proved, apparently, to be devastating. Though American tobaccos contain small amounts of arsenic, its bad effects, if any, are not striking. But the yields of certain soils, especially for the production of cotton, have declined, because of the accumulation of metallic poisons. So also, in some orchard lands, the soil has been contaminated to the extent that it cannot be expected for a period of many years, to produce any useful crop. Fortunately, on a national scale, the acreage thus affected is not large enough to be crippling to our agriculture. The danger of such wholesale applications has been recognized, and the metallic pesticides, in any case, have largely become obsolete.

So matters went until the time of the Second World War. Then—at first, merely as a rumor—began to spread the information about wonderful new discoveries that would inestimably benefit human beings, and perhaps finally swing the balance in their war against insects, and bring victory. Gradually, the name of the chief revolutionary and beneficent substance came to be known, in abbreviation, as DDT. The story circulated of how its wholesale application had pinched out, or prevented, an outbreak of typhus in Naples.

Everyone was ready, after the war, for the new era of comfort and prosperity, with the insects finally put into their place. The dream seemed, for a while, to be coming true. A large part of Greece, a land traditionally plagued by flies, was sprayed by DDT. A long-time resident there described the happiness of that time—"the year without flies." It was too good to be true.

And that, indeed, was just the trouble with it. It was not true. The insects, as some of the shrewder entomologists had already imagined, rapidly developed immune strains. Larger and larger doses of insecticide had to be used, and even they became less and less effective. At the same time, in more sinister fashion, as ecologists began to realize, the DDT itself remained. Chemically, it was highly stable. Biologically, it was a new synthetic material, and so was not palatable to the already-existing organisms of decay. It stayed around—on the land and in the water, and the part of it which seemingly disappeared was found to have gone off into the air whence it came down in rain a continent away from the pests it was meant to kill. Then came a still further disturbing discovery. Many organisms, though they could not destroy DDT, picked it up with their food, and concentrated it. Thus, in the water of an ocean or a lake, DDT might not be detectable, but it was easily detectable in the flesh of crabs and fish. Before long, chemical analysis revealed that every human being, also, was carrying his load of DDT. Either he breathed it in from the air, or he got it, secondhand, from the food that he ate.

There was no reason to think that this load was doing him any good. Certainly, it was not making him immune to the bites of insects. But was it doing him any harm? The question cannot yet be answered. People are not falling down dead with DDT poisoning. But, over the long run of the years, they may be weakened, and their lives may be shortened. (For the end of the story, see our next installment, some thirty or forty years hence.)

Though the story of DDT has been often retold and may be considered well-known, its repetition here has seemed necessary. It was the prototype of all such stories, and there are, unfortunately, many of them.

The decade and a half following the end of World War II provided the heyday for the "new" pesticides. Into their trade names and their chemical constituency, we need not enter. We are concerned with their effects, and their effects are made clear in the designations as 'broad-spectrum," and "nondegradable." Both these terms were offered as descriptives of praise.

"Broad-spectrum" meant essentially "kill-everything." What could be finer? The application of a single pesticide slew not only the particular bug that was troubling a crop, but also could be trusted to kill any other insect pest that happened to be there. What "happened to be there" might include all the insect-eating birds, but that was, so to speak, their lookout. The farmer was slapping the insect that was biting him, and could not stop to think about what he was doing to the balance of nature.

So it was also with "non-degradable." Wasn't this fine, too! It meant that these pesticides resisted chemical and biological decay, and stayed around for a long time—some of them, like DDT, practically forever. The farmer thus gained, it seemed, a kind of permanent protection for his fields. Again, no one considered the disposal problem. Before long, the more careful observers, such as Rachel Carson, began to realize that the effect of these pesticides upon the biological world was massive and devastating, and led on to no one knew what horrifying results.

Silent Spring takes its title from the idea, and it is largely fact, that the singing birds have died off where the pesticides are used, or where their food is affected by the drugs. But the effects of the pesticides upon birds may be much less, in the long run, than the effects upon beneficent insects, and even upon micro-organisms. Honeybees, for instance, have been killed by millions. Moreover, as with DDT, the harmful insects develop resistant strains, and thrive again—hence those billboards with their advertisements to hit them with stronger chemicals.

To the scientists and agricultural experts, however, the "broad-spectrum, non-degradable" ecstasy is as far out of date as a Gatling gun among military experts, or a Sopwith Camel among fliers. Such bug-killers are still being used too much. But they are not for the future. The whole idea of pesticides is yielding to what are known as bioenvironmental methods of control. Some of these are of incredibly subtle sophistication. They must needs be. The insects have shown that they cannot be defeated by mere frontal attack. Before long, pesticides will not be compared to the Gatling gun, but to the bow and arrow. The bug-fighters now deal in such techniques as introduced parasites, environmental manipulation, induced sexual sterility, and the release of individual insects carrying lethal genes. Such methods may perhaps produce a disposal problem, but it will at least be different from that associated with DDT and its fellows. We can only hope that the amount of non-degradable poison already released into the environment is not sufficient to have permanently worsened our habitat.

As of now, pesticides are plentifully used, probably more than they should be. In the future we can expect their use to decline, primarily because of the new methods of control, rather than by restrictive legislation. They will remain in use indefinitely for limited and special purposes, just as no development will ever wholly replace that primitive but useful implement, the fly-swatter.

In any case, when the farmer's wild spree with pesticides comes to an end, no doubt the next problem stands ready to take over. What will be the long-range effects of releasing all those lethal genes? Will induced sexual sterility spread to more than insects? By this time, at least, we should have learned that the insects are doughty opponents. . . .

If field-refuse seems to hold no problem and if pest control methods can be improved, such optimism is, regrettably, not possible with the third basic ingredient. With it, traditional methods have broken down, and no new scientific approach has developed. With manure, that ancient and simple and basic product, everything has suddenly gone topsy-turvy. In terms of historical analogies, the Grand Alliance has at last been broken.

According to widespread beliefs—as recounted for instance, in the story of Cain and Abel—some peoples developed as keepers of flocks and herds, and others undertook the cultivation of the soil. However it may have begun, the distinction soon broke down, and the early civilized peoples were involved both with animal husbandry and field culture. The two, in fact, proved to exist in alliance, not in opposition. The fields produced fodder for the beasts, and the beasts, in their turn, manured the fields, and thus maintained productivity.

In most of the ancient world, winters were mild, so that the flocks and the herds could be kept continuously at pasture in the open. At the proper times, they were permitted to graze upon the stubble. They thus served as their own manure-spreaders, and no problem of accumulation could arise. In the Old Testament there are references to dunghills, but these were probably accumulations of human waste. There is no clear reference to the manuring of fields. In the stables that King Solomon ordered to be built for his chariot-horses, the cleanup men must have been kept busy, but here was a special case. The Gospel of St. Luke, however, presents as a commonplace the idea that one should dig about a tree, "and dung it."

The suggestion that the agricultural practices had improved is probably correct, and one of the influences may have been the Romans. They, in their better days, were highly skilled practicing farmers, and they passed their tradition on to Gaul, Britain, and Europe generally. Some of this tradition survived even the Dark Ages.

Moreover, in the region of cold winters and snow-covered fields, devices were necessary to carry the animals over the winter. Most of them, indeed, were slaughtered in the autumn, and the meat was salted. Still, plow oxen and breeding stock had to be preserved, and they were often penned into byres, in close connection with the living quarters of the family itself. By spring, the accumulation had become considerable, and the regular task thus became to cart the manure out and spread it on the fields. In the fourteenth-century poem *Piers Plowman*, the natural task of a laborer is given as "to take dung a-field."

This tradition made the passage to America and continued in effect clear down into the twentieth century. So-called commercial fertilizers began to play some part from the early nineteenth century onward, but manure remained the great basic product. Only with the period following the Second World War did the shift occur.

As farmers came to be more and more efficiency experts in the production of agricultural products, they came to realize that manure was uneconomic. As compared with commercial fertilizers, it had small plant-nutrient value per ton, generally not enough to pay for its collection and transportation.

The shock of the change came to me suddenly, about 1950, when I heard an Iowa farmer remark, "I can't afford to haul manure more than a mile and a half." The exactness of the words showed that the new agriculture depended not so much on pitchforks as on computers. Moreover, the remark showed that the age-old inter-reliance of animal husbandry and field agriculture was no longer in existence.

Few people are in a position to comprehend the enormity of the shift, as the result of which the traditionally valuable material was thus, with almost dramatic suddenness, transformed into mere waste and refuse, a liability to be got rid of, not an asset to be used or sold.

These are the days of scientific research, when all bright young men are urged to turn their abilities in that direction. Sometimes, indeed, the tasks to which the young scientist must put himself require hardihood. In connection with the present topic, we may thus ask in awe, "Who determined, even to a decimal point, and by what refined methods, the mathematical ratio existing between the weight of human excreta and those of the animals?" Such study, however, has been performed. As a government report states in commendably polite wording, "a cow generates [!] as much manure as 16.4 humans, one hog produces as much waste as 1.9 people, and seven chickens provide a disposal problem equivalent to that created by one person."

Applying these statistics to the known numbers of the various domestic animals, the researchers were able to come up with the gross answer that the "farm" animals of the United States produce ten times as much excreta as do the human beings.

Moreover, there is no sewage system at all, such as exists for at least a considerable majority of the human beings. Where the material is deposited, there it lies, though by the influence of rain a good deal of it, before long, gets into the streams and the ground-water.

During the many centuries of traditional agriculture no serious problem had arisen, partly because manure was collected and returned to the fields. Of even more importance, the animals themselves were widely dispersed, except under a few special circumstances. Horses, cattle, and sheep were normally feeding in pastures. Swine, traditionally, rooted in the woods. Even chickens ranged around considerably, foraging for themselves.

Then, throughout the modern agriculture of the United States, a new method of animal husbandry emerged, in the irrefutable cause of efficiency. The new development showed some curious analogies with the modern trend toward human urbanization, especially with slums.

On the traditional American farm, some hens scratched about in the barnyard, and laid their eggs either in prepared nests, or in their own hiding-places, if they so took the notion. Collecting the eggs was often a child's task, and the marketing of the eggs at the store in town was traditionally the duty of the farmer's wife. At the next stage—say, the early twentieth century—came large specialized operations in the production of eggs, with henhouses set at wide intervals. Finally came the device known as the "battery," in which each pen held a single hen, existing for its whole adult life in the space of a cubic foot or so, thus laying its eggs, its excreta working down through the wire mesh that served as floor. As in a city slum, the concentrations in the new batteries became appalling. Some such establishments house as many as 100,000 hens, and one is reputed to house a million.

Following hard after the development for poultry came similar revolutions in the keeping of other animals. The discovery was made that hogs could also be profitably so concentrated, and "confinement units" are operating which process as many as 10,000 hogs in a year. The prediction is that most of the pork production for the country will soon come from such establishments. Concentrations of turkeys have also proved to be profitable. As for beef-cattle, they are regularly fattened for a period of three to five months in pens where each animal has only about a hundred square feet of space, that is, as much as an ordinary bathroom. (Take a look at your bathroom and try to imagine what it would be like after a steer had been penned and fed there during several months).

To many people this "urbanization" or even "slumiza-tion" of living creatures is somewhat horrifying. Humane societies, or even any decent person, might well doubt as to whether human beings have any "right" thus to oppress their fellow creatures. Any sadist who turpentines a dog or lashes a horse can be arrested and punished. Why should it be permissible, profitable, and even laudable, to confine a hen in lifelong solitary imprisonment, without possibility of exercise, and in revolting fecal conditions? One even wonders whether eggs and meat produced under such conditions can be fully healthful. Such reflections, howev-er, must constitute an aside from the main theme.

As far as disposal is involved, this concentration of

fowls and animals necessarily results in tremendous piles of manure—and, by an unfortunate coincidence, at the very time when there is little market for that former commodity.

The result has been a kind of wild scramble to get rid of the stuff in one way or another. The problem is analogous to garbage disposal, in that no good way exists and so numerous experiments are being tried. A government report lists the possibilities as "field-spreading, composting, anaerobic digestion, incineration, lagooning, dehydration, and other methods." Any kind of method of disposal costs money, and therefore is likely to be shirked. As always, the existence of so many different possibilities indicates that no single good method is available.

Whereas human excreta are handled with some care and at great expense, very little provision has traditionally been made for animal excreta, and there is little legal control. Necessarily, more or less of the material gets into the natural drainage, and begins to affect the streams, much as factory effluents do. Contamination of groundwater, and therefore of wells, is known to occur, and certain human diseases can be traced to such contamination. In dry weather, the dust becomes a hazard. There is also the problem of local nuisance, from smell and unsightliness.

As so often in considering disposal, we sense a lack of coordination in our economic system. Profits are figured, but without the debit of cleaning up afterward. To date, many of these new "food-factories" have been able to operate profitably because at the same time they degraded the environment.

Traditionally, the farmer, as the cornerstone of the economy, has been permitted many bad practices in return for the supreme boon of producing food. In many ways, however, the situation has changed. Farming is less and less a way of life. The modern farmer ("I can't afford to haul manure more than a mile and a half") has become more like a manufacturer. In the future, therefore, the problem of agricultural refuse will probably have to be handled on the analogy of factory effluents.

The particular problem of agricultural disposal is thus, at present, connected with animal husbandry, and the simple accumulation of manure. A concentration of a million hens is the fecal equivalent of a city of more than 100,000 people. But it may exist with nothing resembling a sewage system. These concentrations must be recognized for what they really are, that is, "animal cities." They must not be permitted to remain what they too often are in actuality, that is, "animal slums." They must not be allowed to be overcrowded, filthy breeding-grounds for flies and rodents. They must not be privileged to pollute the streams and blight the landscape, even though the price of eggs may have to rise.

Ultimately, the solution would seem to lie in recycling. If the medieval laborer and his cart are not sufficient to take the dung afield, modern railroads and trucks certainly must be capable of doing so. If the value of the manure does not equal the cost of transportation, then the cost must be added to the price of the product, or the whole method must be abandoned as not soundly economic.

Another possibility is that the manure may be recycled by means of algae or some other biological process, as may also be done with human sewage. Food for the livestock could thus be produced without the intervention of the complicated process of field-culture.

A slight beginning at recycling has actually been made, and a rather curious one. . ... One problem with slaughter-houses has been so-called "paunch-manure," which consists of the large amounts of material in the upper stomachs of the butchered cattle—mostly of hay, and of such a coarse nature as not to pass through sewage systems. It has been a bulky item, difficult of disposal. Recently a process has been developed by which the paunch-manure is cooked and dried, and then fed to other cattle. These seem to relish it, perhaps appreciating its already partly-digested nature.

The recycling of manure itself, however, is still in an experimental stage, and any immediate relief will have to come in other ways. Our Augean Stables call for a Heracles, and for one who will use more civilized methods than merely to clean the stalls by polluting the river.

10

MINERAL REFUSE

"No health or hazard problem"

IF, OF ANY PARTICULAR SITUATION, the proposition can be maintained that it presents "no health or hazard problem," our way of life allows a general relaxation. Public-health authorities wash their hands of the matter, legislatures grant no funds, city fathers exhibit no paternal interest.

Yet such judgments are likely to be superficial, and to mean, at most, only that there is no *immediate* threat of illness or accidental injury. No one looking at a gashed and disfigured landscape will thereby contract an infection, or break an arm. But questions may be raised. The almost brutal dislocations of inanimate nature—do these have also their effects upon the human adjustment? Is such a phrase as "the rape of the land" a phrase only, or does it have psychological implications?

A mountain meadow turned into barren and blistering rockpiles by a gold-dredger, a woodland transformed into barren clay and stone by strip mining—these are much like skeletons. Men have greedily taken what they wanted, the gold or the coal, and have not been concerned with what they did with the leavings. Alienation from the land may have its analogies in alienation from society. In the long run any degradation of the environment, any brutal and irreversible dislocation of the processes of nature, may not be free of health and hazard problems.

Most easily to be dismissed as presenting no threat to welfare are the so-called mineral wastes, as produced by mining, "counter-erosion," and demolition. . . .

Mining is the most ancient of basic industries. Primitive men were digging flints out of stream-banks many thousands of years before they were taming animals or planting crops. But the dirty-faced miner has generally been regarded as a kind of "bad guy." Poets and philosophers have distrusted his "accursed hunger for gold." The farmer, though he had manure on his boots, was conceived as working in a clean partnership with the land, preserving it, year after year. But the miner leaped upon the land like a wild beast, gouged it without mercy, and passed on, leaving it to recover, as best it could, and if it could.

Though the slag-heaps of ancient workings are still observable, early miners operated without power tools and without explosives, and their devastation, by modern standards, was minuscule. Wholesale devastation we may award as an American "first," with the remarkable state of California, as so often, granted the distinction.

The miner of '49, "with his gold pan on his knee," was not able to move much earth. He muddied the streams by digging out the gravel-bars, and his excavations allowed erosion to get started here and there. In every successive year, however, more advanced methods of gold-recovery developed, and they depended upon moving larger and larger amounts of the gold-bearing gravel. By the middle eighteen-fifties, American ingenuity had enlisted the appalling power of water under high pressure, in a process known as hydraulic mining.

By this time the "independent miner" of the early years had largely disappeared, and the same man was working as a hired laborer for a powerful corporation. These corporations piped water from the higher mountains, conveyed it through pipes and hoses, and finally projected it from huge nozzles, known as monitors. The gigantic jets of water played against the auriferous strata which were the loosely-compacted gravel-beds of ancient rivers. These old gravel-beds disintegrated in the blasts of water, and the resulting sludge was run through an intricate set-up of sluice-boxes, so that a little gold per ton of gravel could be extracted. The operation proved to be highly profitable. At least, it was highly profitable as long as no one had to take any account of the disposal of the "tailings."

The gravels lay chiefly on the tops of the more-or-less level plateaus between the deep canyons which such rivers as the Yuba and the American had cut into the Sierran foothills. Hydraulic mining swept away the tops of these plateaus so thoroughly that at the present time the original topography simply cannot be known. Where once the beautiful coniferous forests had grown, there was finally nothing left but a barren expanse of gravel, pebbles and boulders. Only after the passage of a century have the trees and bushes managed, in some degree, to re-establish a cover. Even so, the old "diggings" are still a prominent feature of the landscape.

Tourists, driving along Interstate 80 near Gold Run, see the now-picturesque red cliffs, and their highway actually dips, and runs upon the bottom of the old diggings for a mile or so. Usually the people driving on that highway do not even know what they are seeing. To the south is the floor of the diggings, now partially tree-covered, sloping down toward the canyon of the American River. To the north the red cliffs tower up, the line at which the hoses stopped work, because the railroad followed along the top there.

But the devastation of the forested plateaus was only the half of it, and the less important half. Except for the few ounces of gold to be extracted, all the debris had to be passed on somewhere as tailings. To this end the arrangements of nature were so convenient that the directors of these early companies must even have thought that Providence was favoring them. With a minimum of expense the enormous tonnages of rock and gravel could be washed down into some canyon, a thousand feet or more below, and thus, as far as the companies were concerned, neatly and cheaply "gotten rid of." The country was still thinly settled, and no one seems to have asked who owned the canyons. To have done so would have been to stand in the way of "progress."

As the whole topography was changed on the plateaus, so also it went in the canyon bottoms. Above Dutch Flat, where one of the great gold-workings was located, the canyon of Bear River is V-shaped, narrow, and so "tight" that even a fisherman has difficulty in making his way along it. Below Dutch Flat the canyon has been so filled-in with tailings that it is an almost level floor, a hundred or two hundred yards wide, with the stream meandering across it.

This deposit represents only the coarser material. The silt was swept farther down, as the once-clear Sierran streams became mere channels of mud. The devastation reached clear to the valley, and the Sacramento River, which then constituted the chief artery of transportation for the state, silted up and became difficult for steamboats. As the stream beds were filled in, the rivers began to shift their courses, and floods grew worse. Agriculture, which was developing rapidly,. was adversely affected. Soon, as so often has happened, farmers and miners were embattled.

In the sixties there already were grumblings and complaints. Then, in 1872, the tailings flooded over a small peach orchard, and smothered it out. The owner banded together with some of his neighbors, and brought suit.

On the side of the farmers was a kind of elemental justice; on the side of the miners, everything else. The production of gold was the state's basic industry, and the economy largely depended upon the payrolls of the big corporations. In comparison with the great gold mines, what was an acre of peach trees? No matter what justice and law may have been, the lawyers were able to put up a case, and the embattled farmers lost.

That was only the first exchange of shots. Agriculture was becoming steadily more important in the state, and the troubles caused by the tailings grew worse and worse, and had to be written off as a larger and larger economic loss. Suit followed suit in the later seventies and early eighties. The companies still won, but victory came harder and sometimes was not complete. Costs of litigation became severe.

Attempts to impound the tailings were unsuccessful. Small dams did not do the work, and large dams were too expensive. Movements were initiated to have the dams built at federal expense, a procedure that would have amounted to a subsidy for the companies producing the gold. But Washington did not come to the rescue.

Public opinion, too, was shifting. One would like to think that the people of the state were developing an acuter sense of justice. More cynically, we should probably conclude that economic expediency was changing. Citizens of such towns as Sacramento and Marysville had begun to realize that they did more business with farmers than with miners.

In 1883 the situation approached a climax, and few dramas have ever been more dramatic. The decision was finally entrusted to Judge Lorenzo Sawyer, who himself had been a miner in 1850, and had since risen high as a jurist. He investigated thoroughly. Though he worked on legal principles, he cannot have escaped the economic and social pressures. On January 2, 1884, he read his decision.

Though its complication was such that the legal terminology extended to 250 pages, the decision itself could be summarized in a few words—"The tailings must be impounded."

"Judge Sawyer's decision" immediately became famous. Rarely in the history of the United States has one man's word been so effective and so conclusive. Hydraulic mining was ruined. The gold production of the state dropped by three million dollars in one year. California agriculture swept forward in its triumphant career.

A few operators could afford the impounding of their tailings, and these comparatively small workings lingered on for a while. The gold-dredges, a later development, proved to be more efficient, and they proceeded, for many years, to ruin the aesthetics of the California landscape. After a dredger had, foot by foot, moved across a meadow, nothing was left but neat rows of water-worn boulders, baking in the sun, without bush or tree or blade of grass. Eventually, partly by legal restriction and partly by economic shift, the dredges disappeared in their turn, leaving as their memorial the many square miles of land that they had reduced to a desert of boulders.

The story of hydraulic mining—its dramatic rise and even more dramatic fall—warrants attention, even though it is a century past. It provides a striking example of an industry which could operate by neglecting the problem of disposal, that is, by throwing the responsibility on the public. Hydraulic mining developed when land seemed to be overabundant, and it ended when the pressure on the land became greater. No one, at the beginning, evinced any foresight as to what would be good for the state or the nation, but immediate profit was the goal. In the end, the miners were suppressed, not from any sense of abstract justice, and not from much sense of long-range good to the people as a whole, but chiefly by the development of a pressure group in economic opposition.

As compared with present-day situations, this one of the nineteenth century may seem crude. "Where did those operators," anyone may ask, "get the idea that they could dump all that debris upon land that they did not own, even to the extent of destroying orchards?" Yet much modern operation is as crude, or will seem so in the future. Dumping on land is now fairly well under legal restraint, but dumping into the water of rivers and lakes and dumping into the atmosphere is still very largely taken for granted. . . .

In various parts of the country the chief production of mineral waste has been from open-strip coal mining. When coalseams lie only some feet beneath the surface, operators find it profitable to strip away the overburden, instead of mining by shafts in the older method. Since much coal mining, in any case, has come to be a marginal operation, strip mining cannot profitably expend much money upon proper disposal. The resulting devastation is not as bad as that left by gold-dredgers, but it results in a country that is disfigured and left unproductive for many years. The estimate is that in the eastern United States a million acres have been thus devastated.

Quarries and mines other than coal mines also operate on a vast scale. In a single year, about three and a half billion tons of waste rock and mill tailings are poured out, somewhere, upon the countryside. Like agriculture, however, the mining industry generally has plenty of room. It does not operate in cities, except insofar as it creates its own, as at Butte. A few rivers suffer pollution, but more from smelters than from actual mining operations.

By and large, except for strip mining, the industry seems to offer little problem of disposal. Certain areas, especially in California and in the coal-mining regions, have suffered severely, and in the course of time effort should be expended toward reclamation. Even more strongly, there should be restraint upon their indefinite extension. Coal-miners, no more than gold-miners, should operate by means of throwing the problem of disposal upon the public, and even upon future generations.

In connection with open-strip mining one imaginative suggestion envisages something of the old technique of playing off one enemy against another. To restore the desolation left by strip mining, the cities might begin to use such areas for garbage dumps. By careful planning the surface could be rebuilt, and a fertile soil eventually restored. Such areas, however, are not usually close to large cities, and so a long and expensive haul would be necessary. A beginning at such disposal has already been made, with transportation furnished by specially constructed garbage-trains to run by railroad. . . .

A second important phase of mineral disposal lacks a name, and we may coin for it the term "counter-erosion." Everyone recognizes the bad effects of erosion, but few seem to have focused upon the problem of what becomes of the material which is eroded away.

Along any new highway the cuts soon begin to show runnels like small river-systems. Along a few miles of highway, many tons of earth may wash away. This material is first deposited in gutters and ditches along the highway, and causes trouble. Eventually it gets into the natural drainage, muddying the streams. It tends to throw out of adjustment the natural and long-established balance of the stream-flow. At one place it may clog a stream by a deposit of mud and sand. At another place it may cause the stream to erode more deeply into its banks. If the drainage is unobstructed by lakes or dams, the material starts on a long journey toward the sea, to be picked up and deposited many times over the course of years. More commonly, these days, the silt lodges behind a man-constructed dam, which is thus reduced in efficiency for every cubic yard of silt deposited.

Though highways are probably the chief offenders, all sorts of construction work, logging, and even unskillful agriculture, add to the problem of counter-erosion. The answer of the dam-builders to the threat of silting is to build catch-dams higher up. The better method would obviously be to control erosion.

As with so much, affluence is chiefly to blame. As with other basic commodities, the United States has been so rich in land and soil that it has always been, and continues to be, wasteful. One may contrast the practices in such a country as Japan. Cramped for centuries upon four little islands, the Japanese have learned to treasure and to preserve every coffee-spoon of earth. . . .

The third major phase of mineral waste, and one which has just recently become important, is that of demolition debris. "Urban renewal" has become a slogan of the postwar years, and in the good name of slum-clearance large areas of many cities have been reconstructed. But, to be reconstructed, they must first be laid waste.

Historically, as it happens, demolition debris is a very old phenomenon. In ancient times the life of a city was likely to span not more than a few hundred years. Then, perhaps, earthquake or fire ravaged it. More often, the devastation of war fell upon it. Then its people were killed or driven away as slaves, and the old site lay vacant, as the untended buildings toppled in decay.

Eventually, however, if the site was a good one, other

people came, and built another city there. By that time the mud bricks had gone back into the soil, the roof timbers had rotted, and most of the building stones were so deeply buried as not to be worth the digging out. The new people generally did no more than to level the debris off a little, and then erect their new houses on top of the ruins of the old ones.

With every rebuilding the level of the site rose. In the course of a thousand or two years, what had at first been perhaps a small natural knoll became a good-sized artificial mound. In the Near East these mounds were so much a part of the landscape that the Arabs had a regular word, calling each of them a *tel*—hence such a modern name as Tel Aviv.

Heinrich Schliemann, digging for Troy in such a mound, was appalled when he discovered, not the one city that he had imagined, but half a dozen which he did not want and which were merely embarrassing. In fact, he had further bad luck in that the city which he particularly desired to find was the one which had been most nearly obliterated. With it there was an exception to the rule that the new builder merely leveled the debris off. In this case, the new builders were Romans, a very thoroughgoing people. They actually scraped away the traces of the last-preceding city before they built their own.

Even in ancient times, thus, what we may call demolition-debris created a certain problem, though the gradual rise of the artificial mound might be considered to create a better defensive position.

In the United States the ravages of war, though not unknown (especially in the path of Sherman's army), have never been considered normal. Our reconstruction of cities has generally meant the tearing down of buildings to make room for the construction of larger and better ones.

"In the old days," to use that seductively nostalgic phrase, the material of a demolished building was largely salvaged. Boys got jobs cleaning off old bricks with hatchets. Even nails were often saved.

Then, at some point—whether because of the invention of the iron ball or for some other reason—the balance shifted. Just as it became cheaper to discard an old automobile part rather than to mend it, just as it became more efficient to supply commercial fertilizer rather than to transport manure, so the machine age discovered that it could more easily destroy and discard an old building than it could salvage one. Labor costs, in particular, had become too high. There was, indeed, little possibility of resorting to explosives, and even fire was too dangerous for general employment. But the steel balls began swinging, and the bulldozers began pushing, and the huge "clamshells" began grabbing.

Demolition became an art, and could proceed at fantastic speeds. On one day the citizen might pass a good-sized building that he had known all his life. In a day or two it would have vanished clear away, as if at the rubbing of a lamp the jinns had appeared, lifted it up by the four corners, and whisked it away. Most likely, the citizen never asked a question as to what had become of the materials which had composed the building. Those materials, strictly speaking, were not entirely mineral, because of much wood in the construction. But most of the material was brick and stone, concrete, glass, plaster, and various metals. Also, in the process of demolition and of reconstruction, tons of dirt were scooped up and carried away.

In addition to slum clearance, the construction of freeways has resulted in square miles of devastation. There has also been new construction of all kinds, most of it preceded by demolition or excavation. Under the influence of power-machinery and affluence, a major problem has thus arisen out of nothing.

Historically, the term Levellers applies to a political party of the seventeenth century, which advocated an extreme democracy. Perhaps the modern ball-and-bulldozer men should revive the term for themselves. At the same time they might take as their model the famous though somewhat cryptic words of the prophet Isaiah, "Every valley shall be exalted, and every mountain and hill shall be made low." Their ideal seems to be to "exalt" the valleys by piling demolition debris into all the low places, and to make the hills low by scooping them off with bulldozers.

The answer to the question of what becomes of demolition waste is, in general, that it is merely dumped where it can be dumped most cheaply. Usually it is dumped in low places, and called "fill." Because of the wood involved, it is not the best kind of foundation material, but it may serve. Whether the community is better off for having that particular place filled is usually not a matter to be considered. The "improvement" comes in the new construction; the old material may serve a good purpose, or it may create an eyesore. Moreover, it tends to be basically destructive to land and space, at a time when both are becoming rarer and more prized for the future.

Swamps and tidal flats are particularly subject to fill. Traditionally, they are not much regarded, being blamed for producing mosquitoes, and even bad smells. But, more and more, a case is being made for swamps and tidal flats in the general ecology. They have their own kind of beauty, they shelter and support wildlife of many kinds, they are natural preservers of that ever-rarer commodity "open space."

Since demolition waste is a problem of recent development, it seems especially to call for intelligent consideration. It's various ramifications have received very little attention.

As one approach, city-planners should always consider both ends of the undertaking—not only what is to be built, but also what is to be done with the material removed. It should not merely be dumped in the cheapest way, but should be dumped where it will do the most good, or the least harm, in the future. Some extra expense at the first stage would result in high profits eventually.

In particular, attention should be paid to recycling the material. Road building and other construction work consumes enormous tonnages of rubble of various kinds. Most of this is material which has previously been unused, and is produced from quarries, gravel pits, and similar sources. By proper foresight a larger amount of demolition waste might be channeled into new construction. Careful planning, coupled with imagination, might put some bright ideas to work.

For instance, instead of the mere filling-in of bodies of water, there might be use of fill to increase the complexity of shorelines, with resulting improvement of boating, fishing, and other recreation.

As with most phases of the disposal problem, the solution of the newly-created difficulties of mineral waste requires a mental readjustment. The conception of "something to be got rid of" should be abandoned. Along with it should go the idea of immediate expense. Demolition wastes should be considered, on the one hand, a hazard both to present and to future, and on the other hand, a potential resource.

A saying has it, "War is too important to be left to the

generals." We might also put it, "Demolition is too important to be left to the wreckers."

The unplanned "creation of desolation" is tending to become too much an accepted part of modern life. We must broaden our view of what is meant by "health and hazard."

11

SMOKE

Garbage dump in the sky

TO QUOTE from a literary work entitled *Storm*, now almost old enough to be termed classic, "As a crab moves on the ocean-bottom but is of the water, so man rests his feet upon the earth—but lives in the air."

The passage continues in words that might be considered, as of the time of writing, prophetic, "As water environs the crab, so air surrounds, permeates, and vivifies the body of man. If traces of noxious gas mingle with it, he coughs and his complexion turns deathly gray."

That book was written in 1940, and in that year poisoned air was considered only in terms of gas-warfare, or of some accidental or wholly abnormal occurrence. The human race then had plenty of troubles, especially the onset of a World War, but the circumambient and all-sustaining air presented no appreciable cause for worry. Now, a quarter of a century later, though universal peace still seems as far away as ever, war is quite possibly a less critical problem than air pollution. In the long view of world history, 1945 may not be so much remembered for the ending of World War II as for being the year when the citizens of Los Angeles established one more "world-first," by becoming generally conscious of smog.

Air is so essential to man that he dies if removed from it for about a minute. If even small amounts of pollutants are added to it, he suffers and even dies. One would think, then, that civilization—as collective "man"—would always have been highly sensitive to the maintenance of the purity of the air. On the contrary, the development of civilization, especially of the industrialism of the last two centuries, has made air pollution a part of its progress, being able to pay larger dividends by using the air as a convenient and free dump. The situation has quite possibly become irreversible, that is, the system, perhaps, cannot now be changed without the destruction, or serious crippling, of the civilization that depends upon the system. . . .

As compared with many other disposal questions of present concern, that of air pollution, in its feeble beginnings, is remarkably ancient. It began as soon as man attained some mastery of the art of fire.

Primitive man, as soot-marks demonstrate, built fires inside of caves. His material was dry wood, which is not a smoky fuel. Still, just as the proverb declares that smoke indicates fire, so there is no fire without some smoke. Presumably, a few of these early people suffocated themselves, and many of them may have developed coughs and running eyes. Outside of the cave, however, the air still remained benign for a while.

But even this outside air, before too many centuries had passed, was affected by man's remarkable capacity for fouling his own nest. Burning grassland and woodland, to scare out the game, developed as a regular practice among many primitive tribes. To attain the profit of a few deer or wild pigs, a whole mountainside might go up in smoke and flame, obscuring the sun, smoldering on for weeks.

Over the millenia, evolving in an environment that was well permeated with wood smoke, man adapted and became adjusted. Even yet most people find the smell of such smoke, if not too concentrated, a pleasant one, deeply nostalgic. The chimney was comparatively a late invention, and even in the Middle Ages, a stone hearth was usually built in the center of a room, and the smoke from the open fire found its way out, vaguely, through upper openings. So much of it, naturally, got into the nostrils, eyes, and lungs of the inmates, that there must have occurred, as the generations passed, a kind of racial adjustment. Clear down to the present time, no one has ever raised much complaint about wood smoke.

The situation changed sharply with the introduction of that effective but hellish material known to the English as "sea-coal." They thus distinguished it from ordinary "coal" which was what we now know as "charcoal." The fact that the unmodified term has shifted its meaning would show what happened, even if we did not have plenty of historical records.

The original term arose in London, to indicate that the fuel came in by sea-transport. It came down along the coast from the north, from the mouth of the river Tyne, where the first coal-fields were being developed close to the town of Newcastle. (Thus arose the proverb about carrying coals to Newcastle.)

As early as the thirteenth century, wood was becoming scarce in the vicinity of London, and the new fuel found a ready market. By the end of that century a good deal of it was being used, and there were already some complaints about the smoke. The first regulatory law came in 1306.

One cannot help thinking that this early objection to coal smoke failed to be altogether rational. London had no more than twenty or thirty thousand people, and almost nothing of what we would call industry. Granted that little was known about managing coal fires, so that they smoked badly, still the objections can scarcely have been well based. Undoubtedly there was a bit of superstition involved. The people, understandably, thought that this new kind of smoke, even enough of it just to make the air smell a little, was "bad for you." In the long run, historians will perhaps agree. A thousand years hence, the commonplace opinion may be that the use of coal brought infinite disasters upon the human race. Even now, we may suspect as much, though the general verdict would have to be from the other side.

Possibly the Londoners, who had to breathe this new smoke, had their lives shortened, but what with wars and plagues and malnutrition, life was pretty short anyway. Since people did not fall dead, gasping and catching their throats, and since the price of wood continued to rise steadily, public opinion became reconciled to coal—or to sea-coal, as it was called clear down into Shakespeare's time.

By 1600 most people had become adjusted, or at least reconciled, to coal smoke. There were always, however, some objectors and protestors. Smoke would grow thicker and thicker, and then laws and regulations would be passed, and enforced to some extent. So, cyclically, things got worse and worse—not only in London, but over England in general, as the whole area affected by the smoke became larger. Conditions were kept from becoming intolerable by improvements in methods of burning so that the concentration of smoke in one spot was probably not too severe. For instance, stacks and chimneys were being built higher.

The most interesting document in the case was published in 1661, by John Evelyn, of Balliol College, Oxford. His neo-Latin title, *Fumifugium,* is sufficiently explained by the subtitle *The inconvenience of the Air and Smoke of London dissipated.* Much of the little book has a painfully modern suggestion. Of London, as if describing some American city, he wrote, "When in all other places, the air is most serene and pure, it is here eclipsed with such a cloud of sulphur, as the sun itself, which gives day to all the world besides, is hardly able to penetrate and impart it." Again, he mentioned, as if he were driving toward some modern megalopolis, "The weary traveler, that many miles distant, sooner smells, than sees the city to which he repairs." Also of modern application, Evelyn put special blame upon the industrialists—brewers, dyers, lime-burners, salt-makers, and soap-boilers.

One interesting detail of Evelyn's description is his mention of "sulphur." To be sure, the idea of chemical elements was as yet undeveloped, and such a term was likely to be used vaguely with a generalized unpleasant suggestion. Still, sulfur occurs as a native substance, and was well-known to the alchemists, and its acrid fumes are sufficiently impressive, even if you do not know their chemical formula.

Whether or not Evelyn and his contemporaries knew by any rational means that there was sulfur in coal smoke, they had actually stumbled upon an important fact. As so often, man in his beginnings, had been lucky. His first fuel, which was wood, was really a beneficent one, because wood contains very little sulphur. From the thirteenth century downward, what people disliked about coal smoke, even if they did not know it, must have been, mostly, the sulfur dioxide. Whether these fumes were as bad for them as they feared, may be doubted. But there could be no arguing about the unpleasantness, as each man's nose testified irrefutably.

But when Evelyn wrote, things were just getting started. The full force of the Industrial Revolution struck England in the later eighteenth century, and the smoke plague grew worse and worse, decade by decade. Protests continued, and laws and regulations continued, and methods of coal burning improved tremendously. But the dark pall over each city, London especially, spread and spread. By 1870 the poet William Morris had to call upon his readers to "Forget six counties overhung with smoke."

How much damage was done to the English people can never be determined. One of the basic discoveries about cancer was made in the nineteenth century when a doctor determined that chimney sweeps, regularly exposed to soot, developed cancer of the scrotum. But by this time, after a dozen generations, the Londoners were becoming, both physically and psychologically, as accustomed to the fumes of coal as their ancestors had been to wood smoke.

Damage to property was also heavy. Statuary was eaten away into a gross caricature of its original self. Brick buildings deteriorated in about fifty years. The whole drabness of the Victorian era may be linked with the smoke. Color in architecture was considered a vulgarism, probably because color in architecture was an impossibility. Drab and dark interiors were fashionable because anything else showed dirt. Victorian painters considered browns, grays, and drabs to be the proper colors, even for a landscape.

The story of smoke is particularly that of England, because that is where the story began and developed. Not the rock of Gibraltar but a lump of coal was the cornerstone of the British Empire. Symbolically—or was it even more than that?—the Empire crumbled, along with the coal business.

The use of coal, however, had rapidly passed to other countries, the United States among them. By the end of the nineteenth century, the industrial cities were badly sooted-over, and Pittsburgh, in particular, had become a byword.

Smoke should not, indeed, be altogether attributed to the use of coal. In recent years fuel oil, burned for the generation of electric power, has also contributed its large share.

The problem of smoke in the United States, whether caused by coal or oil, continued well into the twentieth century, then passed a peak, and—with almost dramatic suddenness—ceased to be important. Contemporary discussions of the disposal problem hardly include the word *smoke*.

This shift arises partly from a change in terminology. "Smoke" remains a word for ordinary people, but it is not a valuable term for the expert, because smoke consists of an uncertain and varying mixture of materials, with each of which the expert prefers to deal separately. . . .

One part of smoke (enough for the present chapter) consists of what gives it the dark color, the "particulates." These are the billions of tiny bits of unburned carbon, which form the soot in improperly burning coal or oil fires. There are also, especially from burning coal, the particles of so-called fly ash, that are whirled up through the stacks, and then are borne off by the air currents. Eventually—largely within a few miles downwind from the chimney—the particulates settle out of the air onto the ground or the water surface, thus creating the dirtiness of the smoke problem, and the intolerable nuisance that it has produced, especially for housewives.

Actually there are other sources for the cloud of particulates that settles on the United States. Some of it may even be termed natural—such as particles from far-off volcanic eruptions, ash and soot from lightning-set forest fires, and dust blown off the western deserts. Various human activities add their share, especially agriculture, with its burning and its cultivation of fields in dry and windy weather. But the natural and agricultural soot and dust, as an earlier chapter has already indicated, are produced in widely-scattered areas where population is generally scant. They do not usually occasion more than local and temporary nuisance. The real problem of particulates—or, to return to the popular terminology, of smoke—arises from industry in urban developments.

But even in cities, now, toward the end of the twentieth century—the problem of mere smoke has ceased to be acute. Such centers as Pittsburgh and St. Louis have even achieved remarkable successes in abatement, and at the same time did not bring economic ruin upon their industries.

Perhaps we should congratulate ourselves that we have thus solved a centuries-old problem by good sense, well-planned regulation, and honest enforcement. But such self-satisfaction might be premature, and we might best remain realistic. Our knight in shining armor has overthrown, not a ravaging and man-eating ogre, but a poor old toothless thing, worn down by years of starvation. Coal, as everyone knows, is being used less and less, proportionately, for the production of heat and power. In most parts of the country it has completely vanished from the private home, which has gone over to the clean fuels, chiefly gas and electricity. Many industries and power plants still use coal and oil, but their experts have long since discovered that smoke represents wasted fuel, and that the company may even save money by cleaner combustion. Moreover, with coal taken out of the home and used only in large operations, the problem of enforcement becomes infinitely easier. The situation, in fact, is much like that of the liquid effluents from factories, and they, we have seen, are already on the way toward control.

Smoke is even more easy to control than liquid effluents, because it proclaims itself to all the world. A stream of water running from a factory into a river or a sewer is not conspicuous, and the connivance of an official inspector may be arranged. But black smoke belching from a high stack stands out against the sky for every voter to see. The housewife in particular bristles up in wrath, and a politician recognizes a good vote-getting issue. If the smoke were colorless and odorless, would campaigns against it be successful?

Yet that may not be a fair question. If smoke were colorless and odorless, would there be any reason for campaigns against it? Possibly a threat to public health would remain, but it would be hard to prove. Also we should remember that the emissions of chimneys and stacks include various gases as well as the particulates, and these too, in the largest sense, would have to be included as part of smoke.

These gases, however, are basically different from the particulates. The latter are merely carried along in the current of the air, as a twig floats down a river. The very finest particles may float around for a long time, but they are never really a part of the air, any more than the twig is part of the river. They are solids, and the atmosphere, which consists of gases, tends to get rid of them by the mere process of fall-out, that is, by the working of gravity, just as, we may also put it, the atmosphere by the same force of gravity deposits on the ground a beer can thrown from a car window.

But the fumes that pour out as a part of the smoke (or along with the smoke, if that is a preferable way of thinking) are gases like the rest of the atmosphere and they become a part of it, just as the raindrops that fall on the surface of the water become a part of the river. The man-made gases in the atmosphere, thus, produce a different problem from that of the particulates, and make necessary some consideration of the nature of the atmosphere itself.

12

SMOG

The knife at the throat

EARTH, WATER, AIR, AND FIRE were the four elements of the ancients. The moderns have altered the meaning of *element*, and even in their non-scientific conceptions they have deposed fire from such high estate. But the other three remain basic. Especially as regards disposal, everything must be "committed" to one of these three.

Of the three, air is the most selective. You cannot throw old automobiles bodies into it, to be wafted away. You cannot use it to get rid of manure, except by some very roundabout process. But all other means of disposal have their limitations too. A sewer-pipe carries a certain amount of sewage perfectly, but if required to carry too much it first gurgles and bubbles, and then merely refuses, letting the sewage flow where it may.

Within its limits, the atmosphere is even a highly effective and efficient disposal agent. Taking up particulates from any source, the atmosphere diffuses them widely, carries them along in its winds, and finally lets them fall out thinly over a wide area, and thus return to the soil. The atmosphere absorbs gases, and liquids evaporated to be gases, and also diffuses these widely. Then, in due time, the water vapor condenses out as rain, and the gases are largely washed out in solution. By thus being able to get rid of pollutants, the atmosphere has a considerable capacity to protect itself.

At least we may consider this to have been the traditional or "evolutionary" history of the matter. For, much more than either the land or the ocean, the atmosphere came into existence and continues to exist by a system of checks and balances. It is always in a state of flux.

About four-fifths of it consists of largely inert gases, chiefly nitrogen, and does not change much. The other three chief ingredients are oxygen, carbon dioxide, and water vapor, and they are constantly being poured in and run out again. In addition, during millions of years of natural development, both physical and biological processes have been adding vast amounts of other gases, some of them those which we would term noxious. Volcanic eruptions have contributed different unpleasant constituents, including some of the sulfur oxides and the highly poisonous carbon monoxide. Glowing charcoal left at the end of forest fires also added its share of carbon monoxide. The processes of decay, particularly in marshes, produced marsh gas, and people talked about an odorous "miasma." The smell may have been largely from hydrogen sulfide, and that gas was produced, and still is, by the normal digestive processes of animals and human beings, being got rid of daily in vast aggregate amounts, along with other gases, by that ancient process known politely as "breaking wind."

The atmosphere was not polluted by these naturally-generated gases, though some of them were poisonous. They were washed out in the rain, or burned into something harmless when they touched lightning or flame, or they were re-absorbed by plants or animals.

Undoubtedly, the atmosphere has had a different composition during different geological periods. (That is, more particularly, a topic for a later chapter.) But, in the human period, the atmosphere can be well described, like so much else, as continually changing and continually remaining the same thing. At least, we may say that it so remained until modern industrial civilization came upon the world. Then, at some point, the atmosphere became like the overcharged sewer pipe, and it began to receive certain materials faster than it could get rid of them. The result was—in one syllable—smog. . . .

As a word, *smog* was coined in the twentieth century, being an obvious blend of *smoke* and of *fog*. The word has had a triumphant career. The chief trouble with it is that its suggestion has proved to be wholly inaccurate. As a great amount of highly technical research has demonstrated, fog has really nothing to do with the case, and smoke, as such, very little. Yet, abetted by the word itself, the public still thinks largely in terms of fog and smoke, and even the compilers of the most recent large dictionary, though advertised as smartly up-to-date, merely devote one conventional line to the word, presenting it archaically, much as if they were to define *car* as a *two-wheeled chariot*.

As of the present time, one hesitates, for fear of presenting the obvious, to offer an external description of smog. So to do, for the great majority of the American people, would be like setting out to describe an automobile or the game of baseball. For the benefit, however, of our Eskimo fellow citizens and some dwellers in the more remote islands, one might state briefly that smog is a fog-like, haze-like stuff, with a characteristic yellow undertone, that gets into the air so thickly as even to cut visibility. It makes your eyes run and irritates your respiratory passages.

Smog, like so much else, is the monstrous progeny of urban concentrations, affluence, and the modern capacity to manufacture vast quantities of "unnatural" materials that are tenacious of life.

As an actual problem, smog started in Los Angeles during the sudden boom following the end of World War II. During a few years people considered it a sort of special property of Los Angeles, and dwellers in Southern California could even speak of it with a kind of inverted pride. It obviously was tied up in some way with their having so many people and so much industry and such a high standard of living. At a certain point, however, it passed being a joke.

Besides, smog began to appear in other California cities and soon had to be recognized as a state problem. Even San Francisco, for all that the wind was supposed to blow through the Golden Gate, had its smoggy days. During the same years, too rapidly for anyone's comfort, smog began to show up in other states. It became a national problem.

The trouble in these first years was that no one knew even what smog was or what was causing it. The first idea of mixed smoke and fog, as serious investigators soon realized, was far too simple. In a mixed pack the politicians and the scientists then set out to run the monster down, the politicians yelping loudly, and the scientists with their noses to the ground. Before long they were barking loudly at a particular tree, which proved to be the wrong one. They went on to another one, and so it continued for several years. First, smog was blamed on the manufacture of synthetic rubber; next, on oil refineries. Then there was a wild theory that smog was "manufactured" by natural process somewhere out over the ocean, and blown in to the Los Angeles basin. Then household burning was blamed, and laws were passed to keep people from using backyard incinerators. Finally, however, the scientists managed to get together a considerable body of solid fact about smog.

Basically, when the smog problem became acute, four questions called for answers. What is it? What causes it? What, in turn, does it cause? What measures should be taken?

After twenty years of research, the expenditure of much money, and a considerable amount of acrimonious debate, answers have been supplied for the first two questions, and we may think the answers to be sufficiently accurate and reliable, although there is always the possibility of further refinement. Something certain, though by no means everything, is known also about the effects of smog. As to the final question, that is, what measures toward control should be taken, since we know what causes smog, we know that to remove the causes would remove the smog. At the same time, unfortunately, we have to recognize that the removal of these causes, by any kind of sudden legal fiat, is simply impossible.

As to what smog is, as much research has finally been able to demonstrate, smog itself consists of certain gases which are not natural to the atmosphere, at least in their present quantities. These gases are chiefly carbon monoxide, the oxides of sulfur and of nitrogen, and certain of the hydrocarbons. In addition to the man-produced basic components, certain other compounds are formed from them in the air itself under the influence of sunlight. The most important of these is that three-atomed molecule of oxygen known as ozone.

The inclusion of ozone is this line-up of criminals always strikes older people as particularly odd. They were brought up to think that ozone was synonymous with the very best and freshest of air, so that you took a brisk morning walk in the mountains to get your lungs "full of ozone." Fortunately none of these brisk walkers actually got their lungs full of ozone, or they would have died immediately.

Besides the five main components, or groups of components, there are other constituents, such as fluorides and ketene, and these and others may in the long run prove to be of importance. Still, the experts agree pretty well upon what smog is.

As to the second basic question, the experts are in fair agreement as to what is causing it. First, there is transportation, that is, its almost universal motive power, the internal-combustion engine. Second, there are factories of many kinds and plants for generating electricity, together with the considerably less important heating plants and garbage-incinerators. As a catchall term, at some expense of accuracy, we may include all the non-transportation causes under the term "industry."

Also known, even in the present stage of partial knowledge, is the proportion of the shares of the two contributors. Transportation supplies nearly all of the carbon monoxide (more than 90 per cent of it), two-thirds of the hydrocarbons, and something more than one-third of the oxides of nitrogen. On the other hand, it contributes only an inconsiderable share (about 2 per cent) of the oxides of sulfur. Industry necessarily supplies the rest of it, that is, a small proportion of the carbon monoxide, nearly all the oxides of sulfur, a third of the hydrocarbons, and two-thirds of the oxides of nitrogen.

Even some greater breakdown is possible. Transportation now is based almost entirely upon power derived from petroleum, and chiefly by two types of engine. There is the "ordinary" engine, which provides power for the family automobile and the smaller trucks. Then there is the diesel, which is the power plant for steamships (still so-called), locomotives, larger trucks, and a very occasional smaller car. Unfortunately for the peace of mind of most people, the ordinary automobile produces nearly all of the especially dangerous carbon monoxide. The diesel, however, not to be thought shirking, ejects through its exhaust-pipes a considerable proportion of the oxides of nitrogen. On the other side, in industry, coal—still greatly used for the generation of electricity—is the chief producer of the oxides of sulfur.

As to the effects of smog, our knowledge is still at the elementary level. Such ignorance is only to be expected. The problem of smog has become acute only within the last twenty years, and many of its effects may not even as yet be manifest. Moreover, in the immense and intensely complex system that is life—animals, plants, bacteria—smog is probably working at millions of points which cannot yet, possibly, have become apparent.

Smog is known to injure or destroy many growing plants. "Spectacular damage" has been noted for such diverse crops as cotton and orchids. Because of ravages from smog, the growing of leafy vegetables has almost ceased in the once-productive region around Los Angeles. In the San Bernardino Mountains of southern California severe damage has occurred among pine trees clear up to the 7,000-foot level.

The list of adversely affected plants, as already proved, grows long and even suspiciously diverse—citrus fruits, alfalfa, grasses and other forage crops, tobacco, grapes, spinach (especially sensitive), lettuce, grains. In fact, one can use the word "suspicious" because a suggestion arises that *all* plants may be adversely affected. If a case may be made for such a mixed lot as those already mentioned, the thought arises that damage to other species may not yet have been reported, merely because biologists have not had time to get around to observing it.

Animals seem to be tougher. There is, however, much evidence for the deterioration of cattle when exposed to heavy smog. A study of a large urban zoo even indicated that the wolves and lions developed a tendency toward lung cancer.

Since civilization and the life of man is absolutely dependent upon plants and animals, the case against smog, and even the crisis that has arisen, should be sufficiently proved by its effect upon non-human life. Economically, the situation can be expressed in the crude form of dollar value. A vague-enough estimate is that air pollution costs each person in the United States $65 a year, which amounts to a total charge of thirteen billion dollars annually.

Since modern human beings live highly complicated lives, the effect of smog upon their health is difficult to appraise. Lung cancer is on the increase, and smog may be a cause, but statistical proof is almost impossible. There is more than a suspicion, and at least some evidence, that smog either helps to cause, or exacerbates, both bronchitis and emphysema.

Few people, however, are inclined to argue the matter,

unless they are public-relations experts for some area that is smog-infested. On a mere common-sense basis, most people do not believe that their bodies are benefited by the continual breathing of even small amounts of such poisons as ozone and carbon monoxide, and such irritants as the acid-forming oxides of sulfur and nitrogen. Even if the daily ration does not make you just curl up like a smog-blighted spinach leaf, "it stands to reason" that you are likely to get some bad effects.

Moreover, there is no arguing at all with the inconvenience, the unpleasantness, and even the oppressiveness, of a badly smogged day. No one wants to have his eyes run, and his nostrils tingle, and to be burning his headlights at noon.

At the other end of the scale, there is the actual record of certain known disasters. Usually, as at the factory town of Donora in Pennsylvania, they were caused by some particular pollutant, and not by smog in general. But that is little comfort, and in many American cities, a particularly bad combination of circumstances might, in any year, bring people to clutching at their throats and falling on the floors. Such cities have cut their margin of safety too fine. In a sense, what we should really have, is what we actually may have—a spectacular disaster. If a thousand people died in the street in one afternoon, and ten thousand were hauled off to be laid in hospital corridors, real action would result. Those who died would be the martyrs. As it now goes, many millions of people may be dragging along at a reduced level of activity, failing to get the most out of their lives, because the American dream has vanished somewhere behind a yellowish, ill-smelling haze.

To the present time, there has been too much tendency to consider smog as a local problem, affecting certain regions, notably Southern California, because of overcrowding and especial climatic conditions. That region, it was known, suffered from a kind of mysterious atmospheric condition called an "inversion."

This theory, a very comfortable one for non-Southern-Californians, ceases to be comforting when one takes a look at the map of the country displaying "atmospheric ventilation." Nearly half of the United States, including the areas where nearly all of the people live, is subject to periods of "reduced" ventilation. During such periods, bad smog conditions can rapidly build up, as they did in New

York City during a few critical days in November, 1966. Moreover, just as the outskirts of one city are beginning to touch on the outskirts of another, so one city is beginning to pass its smog on to the next.

Finally, we must remember, the United States has no monopoly upon the production of smog. The automobiles and chimneys of Europe and Asia and the other continents are also busily at work. Osaka and Tokyo are in as bad state as are the American cities. The famous wind which blows in from the Golden Gate is probably bringing with it some of the pollutants that it picked up in Japan.

The final and double-barreled question about smog is, "What is being done about it—actually, as of now; potentially, as future development?"

In the first place, we must rule out any kind of artificial change of climate. The breaking up of an inversion is far beyond human power at present, and far beyond anything that can be as yet projected for the future. Besides, such tamperings with natural processes are dangerous. We might alleviate conditions in Southern California only to find something much worse happening somewhere else.

There have also been ideas about changing the configuration of the land. A gigantic trench or even a huge tunnel, say certain optimists, might be dug through the mountains to sluice off the air with its burden of smog from the coastal lands of California. It would, however, be a ruinously expensive operation, and there would be no guarantee that it would work. Even if it helped the situation in coastal California, it might make things worse elsewhere. Once again, there is no easy solution.

The problem with industry is the less difficult part. Airborne effluents pass out of stacks and chimneys much as liquid effluents run out through pipes. The chimneys are much more conspicuous than the pipes, and cannot well be hidden, even if there is no smoke. They are limited in number, even in a good-sized city, not reaching very many thousands. They are thus, without too much difficulty, controlled by legislation and policing, and the engineers have developed techniques by which the offensive gases can be "scrubbed" out. Such cleaning up runs into expense. As with liquid effluents, however, only the marginal operators need to be much concerned, because the expense can generally be passed on to the consumer.

Diametrically different is the problem offered by transportation. The very fact of mobility makes any kind of regulation difficult. Besides, the sources are numbered, not in thousands, but in millions. Transportation does not have its analogies with liquid effluents, but with the myriad-source problems, such as sewage, garbage, and litter. But also, most serious of all, the technical problems have not as yet been solved.

For simplification, "transportation," from here on, may be taken to mean vehicles propelled by internal-combustion engines on the highways—private cars, buses, and trucks. We may even, for still greater simplification, include all three under the simple term "automobile."

After twenty years of research, smog has been recognized as critically dangerous to the nation, and the responsibility for it has been laid, chiefly, upon the automobile, that is, upon its power plant—whether the ordinary spark-ignition engine or the diesel. Still other types of gasoline engines are possible, and some experimental work with them is progressing. All differ, one from another, as smog producers. Since the diesel, for instance, produces almost no carbon monoxide, the smog problem would be somewhat relieved if that engine became universal. But, in that case, we should have more of the nitrogen oxides. To replace the present engines with diesels, or those of any other type, would be prodigiously expensive, of doubtful final utility, and, in any case, would take years.

Another approach is to accept the engine as it is (and indeed, at the moment, we can scarcely do anything else), and then to purify the exhaust gases.

The engineers start with one great advantage. Nearly all of the objectionable matters pass out through the tail pipe, so it should be possible, one would think, to design a filter which would fit around the exhaust pipe, much as the muffler does. Such a solution has not been possible, for two reasons. First, the amount of material passing through the tail pipe from a running engine is so large that no filter can handle it for any length of time without being larger than the car itself. Second, the gases passed off by the engine are of such various chemical natures that two or three filters in series would be necessary to remove them all.

There has been even, we might say, a third difficulty in that there was no time. Scientists needed a few years more to experiment, and engineers needed a few years after that to evolve practical designs from the scientists' equations. But parts of the country were beginning already to choke (almost literally) on smog. The most immediate palliative seemed to be the so-called "direct-flame afterburner." As a solution, however, this was a halfway measure if there ever was one. In fact, it could better be described as a quarter-way measure, or even a tenth-way measure. It was required only for new cars, and so would become effective only after the passage of several years. Its installation in new cars could be enforced, but there could be little means of enforcing whether it continued to work properly, once installed.

Besides, the device itself was only about 50 per cent effective. It got rid of more than half of the carbon monoxide, along with about four-fifths of the hydrocarbons, and did not touch the oxides of nitrogen at all.

No one but an all-informed optimist could consider that the afterburner had solved the smog problem. Some experts even feared that the afterburners might make things worse. Because of the great complexity of exhaust gases (not to get into the chemistry of it), there may be two materials thrown off which we can call A and B, both noxious. Fortunately, after they get out into the air, A and B tend to unite into AB, which is harmless. Obviously, if there is really any such thing as "obviously" about smog control, if you take A out by means of an afterburner, you leave B around loose to affect peoples' throats and lungs.

Generally, however, what you could say about the adoption of the afterburner was that it might accomplish enough to give the worst-affected parts of the country a temporary respite. As for the future, there seems to be only one realistic answer, "The internal-combustion engine must go!"

Only a few years ago such a statement would have seemed insanity or incredible faddism. Now, however, even the large automobile manufacturers are giving publicity to their search for the electric car, and are beginning to put models on the market.

Thus started, we can expect rapid movement. A curious psychology exists among numerous people that the gasoline car can never be superseded because "Detroit" would fight the replacement. Actually the opposite would seem to be true. Any industry, looking to its own profit, should welcome a happening that renders all its previous products obsolete and at the same time permits it to manufacture new ones. Possibly the electric car will never be everything that the gasoline car has been. It may not be able to go from a standstill to eighty miles an hour in an incredibly small number of seconds. It may not be able to go fast enough to permit illegal speeds easily. Just possibly, however, and for those very reasons, the world may be a better place. In any case, the capacity of the internal-combustion engine to produce poisons seems to have destroyed its usefulness for civilization.

The social and economic impact of the change will be spread over a decade or two. The chief economic opponents, one would think, should be the oil companies. With little market for gasoline and diesel fluid, they would be reduced to producers and marketers of fuel oil, and might not be able to compete with other sources of power. The chief beneficiaries would probably be the producers of electric power, whether they generate that power from the atom, from falling water, or from fossil fuel.

Probably everyone is inclined to grant the eventual necessity of eliminating smog. The great problems arise in connection with how and how soon it must be done, granted that the situation in different parts of the country is not equally critical. A good deal of expert opinion suggests that in the more smog-infested areas there is not much time left, in comparison with the tremendous economic and social inertia to be set into motion.

The mildly-worded ideas of the present discussion seem pale beside the proposition recently maintained by Frank M. Stead, Chief, Division of Environmental Sanitation, California State Department of Public Health, writing in the Winter 1966-67, issue of *Cry California*. He states flatly and in italics that by 1980 every gasoline-powered engine that emits hydro-carbons and oxides of nitrogen must be off the highways and streets of California. He advocates that at the present time legal notice should be served to this effect.

Whether the politicians and the people of the state have the mere guts thus to face the problem seems doubtful. Some cars are already on the road which would still, in the usual course of events, be running in 1980. The economic and social change of the shift would be more severe than those effected by the Emancipation Proclamation. One may doubt whether any people can thus discipline themselves, in the mere prediction of disaster. We must remember that an adequate electric car is, as yet, not even on the drawing-boards. Even after it is designed, it will have to be manufactured in millions, and the expense of replacement will run into many billions of dollars.

The actual procedure may be that California—and other parts of the country too—will have to experience the disaster.

A few palliatives, to gain time, may be suggested. Gasoline rationing, as in wartime, would be a possibility, though one flinches from the certainty of chiseling and black-marketing. The reduction in the average size of engines, enforced by confiscatory taxation in the form of licensing, would also be a help. Development of public transportation is an obvious line of advance, but such planning and construction itself takes years, and so far, in the United States, the private car has been replacing public transportation. A reversal of a deeply-rooted folk-habit, involving individualism and status, is so difficult as not to be expected. . . .

Even the removal of the internal-combustion engine will not bring about a golden era of pure air and sparkling blue skies. Shrewd planning will still be necessary. For instance, there has recently been inaugurated, from the highest of motives, the project of improving the economic condition of the mountain region known as Appalachia. In our civilization, the obvious remedy for economic ills is the establishment of industry. But the long and narrow valleys between ridges that are characteristic of the Appalachian area suffer from atmospheric inversion and persistently reduced ventilation. In fact, in such conditions, the region is second only to the coastal plain of Southern California. Donora is at the northern tip of Appalachia, and its disaster of 1948, when hundreds were ill and twenty died, is an indication of the results that might be expected from the industrialization of that mountainous area, which might better, for the benefit of the country in the long run, be allowed to grow timber, and serve as an area of recreation. . . .

The air will continue to be a highly efficient disposal agent within its limits. It will continue to absorb, diffuse, and redistribute immense quantities of gases produced by natural processes. It can even handle a certain load of the unnatural gases, as produced by civilization.

In the end, we might return to proverbial wisdom, and quote, of the atmosphere, "A good servant, but a poor master." We might also add, "Don't work a good horse to death"—in this case, "your own death."

Thus to employ such an ugly and even un-American word as "death" may seem to some people as a descent into hysterical, scarehead tactics. Actually, this present account—over-simplifying, in the attempt to attain some readability—has possibly failed to give an impression of the variety of the poisons that are being poured into the air, any one of which might prove, at a certain point, to be immediately dangerous to human life or to produce a seriously adverse effect upon some link in the vastly complicated chain of cause-and-effect upon which civilization depends.

A recent White House report presents a list of these horrors—not to be immediately eliminated, but merely to be investigated, since at present we are merely pouring them into the air without knowing what the effects may be. As of "highest priority," the list includes: "Sulfur dioxide, carbon monoxide, carbon dioxide, fluoride, ozone, sulfuric acid droplets, oxides of nitrogen, carcinogens (various types), peracyl nitrates, gasoline additives including lead and asbestos particles."

As of merely "high priority," the list continues, "benzene and homologues, alkyl nitrates, alkyl nitrites, aldehydes, ethylene, pesticides, auto exhaust (raw), amines, mercaptans, hydrogen sulfide, and beryllium particles."

The possibility is that any one of these substances may reach a concentration where it would be catastrophically harmful. The probability is, their number considered, that at least one of them will do so.

Two of them, currently, seem to be especially dangerous. . . . Nearly all gasoline contains compounds of lead as an "anti-knock" additive. This lead in the form of various compounds streams out through the millions of exhaust-pipes. Though not actually a part of the smog, these compounds stay in the air of cities long enough to be breathed in. Lead is a slow poison—especially a threat to human fertility. Recent investigations show that modern Americans in general, and not only painters, are carrying an unnatural load of lead. Moreover, city-dwellers carry more of it, per person, than do the now comparatively few country folk. The investigators assure us that these concentrations of lead need not, at the present level, cause alarm. But what will be the situation in the next generation, among those who, all their lives, have been breathing the ever-thicker air of larger and larger cities?

Then there is the curious situation with ozone. At some quiet time in the past, the best authorities set the "tolerance limit" at 0.1 part per million. This tolerance limit is now regularly exceeded in all major cities!

As regards all these exotic substances that civilization is discarding into the air, we cannot make any final judgment, but we can at least congratulate ourselves upon two points. First, man seems to be a tougher animal than the experts are inclined to think. Second, man seems to be blessed with amazing luck—at least, it appears so far—at not having already killed himself by his practice of releasing things first and then considering the consequences afterward.

13

THE ULTIMATES

CO_2 and atomic wastes

CIVILIZATION exists by the expenditure of power, and modern American civilization requires amounts of power, ever increasing, that are fantastic by any previous standards. There seems to be no possible escape from the demands for more and more power as long as we expect civilization to keep moving faster and faster for the needs and desires of more and more people. The curve of used power even has a tendency to rise, not by an ascending straight line, but by a parabolic curve, as Henry Adams emphasized half a century ago.

The only way for us to escape this tyranny of power would be to reduce the population, renounce some of our affluence, and settle back into the quieter life that we lived in earlier years. Since we show no sign of doing even any one of these things, we must go on producing power and taking the consequences. One of the consequences involves disposal—in fact, what may be termed two ultimate disposal problems. . . .

Since all of the important present sources of power involve the use of matter of one kind or another, the Law of the Conservation of Matter insures that the power industry is left with what may be called "refuse," though not always with a "problem."

The chief present sources of power are water falling by gravity, the combustion of the "fossil fuels," and atomic fission. Power from wind, tides, sunshine, and animal and human muscle are too minor at present to be counted, though some of them offer possibilities for the future, along with atomic fusion.

Historically, the generation of power by falling or running water developed over a thousand years ago with little mills for grinding grain. Water-driven sawmills probably came next. Engines driven by fossil fuel—originally, coal—have been doing their share for two centuries or a little more. Atomic power has been developing in the last decade. . . .

Of the three major methods, waterpower is by all odds the neatest, and can even be termed the most attractive and most appealing. Water, as it runs to the ocean, is made to pass through power plants. This process does not change the water, and it is then passed on intact, for making more power below, or for any or several or many of the other uses to which civilization puts it. Most power plants must have especially constructed conduits or canals to get their "refuse" water started on its way to the ocean again, but this necessity is so minor as scarcely to constitute a disposal problem.

The only trouble with waterpower is that there can never be anything like enough of it to run civilization. . . .

The invention and development, chiefly in England, of the coal-powered steam engine inaugurated the modern age. Unwittingly, the developers of the steam engine also inaugurated what has been called a vast geophysical experiment.

Coal, and then oil and natural gas, began to feed more and more furnace fires. The disposal problem first became apparent with smoke, and later and more subtly with the constituents of smog. After a while both of these seemed to be controllable, with great expense, but within the limits of man's capacity. But there remained still one of the two ultimate problems of disposal.

All the "fossil" fuels deserve that name because that is just what they are literally. Chiefly derived from the plants, they represent carbon and its compounds, once taken from the carbon dioxide of the atmosphere. To "extract" the power, man burns the fuels, thus combining their carbon with the oxygen of the air to produce again the gas, carbon dioxide, which the plants had once extracted from the atmosphere, hundreds of millions of years past.

In the Carboniferous era, when most of the coal-beds were formed, the atmosphere presumably was much richer in carbon dioxide than it is now. But, by burning the fossil fuels, we are rapidly—that is, in the process of decades—turning the atmosphere back into something resembling that of the Carboniferous era. Essentially and in a world-wide sense, we thus face what may be considered the greatest and the least solvable of all disposal problems.

Curiously, there appears to have been, so far, no problem at all. Once more, we might say, the luck that seems to have worked for the human race, has taken the matter in charge. When scientists lately got around to figuring how much the increase of carbon dioxide in the atmosphere should be, on the basis of the fairly accurate knowledge of how much fossil fuel has been burned, they found a discrepancy. There was not so much of that gas as there should have been. The most likely theory is that it has been dissolved in the upper layers of the ocean. So, the effect of the change in the atmosphere has at least been postponed.

As to what the carbon dioxide may do to the ocean, if it is really there—that is still another question. No one knows what it may do to life in salt water, and for all we know another catastrophic change is in the making.

Increased carbon dioxide in the air stimulates the growth of some plants, but not much of it is being absorbed in this way. Over most of the earth other factors set the limitation to the growth of plants—for example, water. The deserts are not going to bloom and burgeon just because there is more carbon dioxide in the air.

The gas is inert and harmless to air-breathing animals, including man. Its proportion in the air could double or triple without its affecting anyone's breathing. In its effect upon man, the ticklish aspect of the situation is the possibility of major alterations in climate.

As far as this particular gas is concerned, not its chemical properties, but its physical properties create the difficulty. Carbon dioxide transmits, in the air, the short wavelengths of sunlight, but not the long wavelengths. Accordingly, it traps heat by the process known in the archaic language of scientists as "greenhouse effect." In the modern world, people know rather little about greenhouses and a good deal about automobiles. So we might rather call it "closed-car effect," since everyone knows the way in which even gentle sunlight builds up the temperature inside a closed car, glass being like diffused carbon dioxide in transmitting the short rays, and then blocking their exit when they have shifted into long rays.

Quite possibly the process has effected already a slight rise of the earth's average temperature. There is some evidence to this effect.

At first thought, most people think that such an increase in the average temperature would really be "a good thing." It might, they can see, open up large areas of the Arctic to human habitation. The trouble is that an increase of temperature could make other regions less inhabitable. Moreover, the whole pattern of world climate, of winds and rainfall, would probably shift. Even granting that the world as a whole might be a more beneficent place for man, it would not be the same place, and the political and national reverberations would be revolutionary. What would happen if the United States and China became unable to support their present populations, and at the same time great empty and inviting spaces in Canada and Siberia became available?

The most immediate problem, however, would be the melting of the ice, particularly in Antarctica. In the geological time-scale the earth has passed—as it were, only yesterday—through four glacial periods. Even the comparatively small change produced by man's burning of the fossil fuels may trigger the situation, and set the ice to melting still farther. The change of the polar ice to water could raise the level of the sea by four hundred feet, and destroy the homes and agricultural lands of perhaps half the people of the world. Such a process could not happen overnight, and it might require a millennium. But a rise of only one or two feet, such as might happen in a few years, would cause worldwide damage to harbor installations, coastal cities, and low-lying lands.

As to what men can do to solve this ultimate disposal problem, the answer is simple—"Essentially, nothing." With luck—and man, throughout the last million years, has been an inordinately lucky animal—with luck, then, the ocean may absorb most of this carbon dioxide, or something else may happen. Tropical swamps may suddenly flourish with rank vegetation, as they did in the Carboniferous era. But this increased growth-rate would make an appreciable difference in the total amount of carbon dioxide, unfortunately, only in the course of many thousands of years. Any loose calcium or magnesium lying about has the property of fixing the carbon dioxide into rock, but there is not any vast amount of these elements not already so fixed. Dust in the atmosphere diminishes the effect of the sun, and by spewing out more and more smoke, we might balance the heat off. But the effects upon plants, animals, and man would probably be deleterious. Unless help arrives from somewhere, our descendants in the next few centuries may be huddling closer together, upon shrinking continents.

Curiously, however, just as the redskins seemed to have us at their mercy, it turns out that the cavalry is galloping to our rescue, and is just beyond the hill. Atomic power may offer the solution. . . .

As to whether atomic power can assume, and maintain, the load of power production now carried by the fossil fuels, that is a question for the future, and the scope of this present book is sufficient without entering into prophecy. Possibly also, the scientists and engineers may effect some new and ingenious method of power production, such as the direct generation of electricity from sunlight, or extensive use of tides.

In any case, the use of atomic power has begun, and is developing rapidly, and it provides its own ever-increasing disposal problem. In this connection, however, we face something almost unique in the history of the world. The problem is being recognized and considered, not after it has developed, but before—or almost!

There may, of course, be some argument about the matter. Some people believe that the release of atomic waste has already injured the environment and adversely affected the human race. But such a conclusion is impossible to demonstrate. On the other hand, tremendous efforts have already been expended, and vast sums of money spent, in disposing of atomic wastes, and in working upon means to do so more advantageously.

The contrast with other areas of the whole problem is tremendous. No one did anything about litter until litter had become offensive. No one worried about factory effluents until the rivers began to stink. No one bothered about the exhaust from internal-combustion engines until smog made the eyes run. An optimistic philosopher, from our handling of atomic waste, might even argue that mankind had learned something from experience, and was at last becoming foresighted and reasonable. Again, let us remain rational, and even cynical. The better approach toward the problem of atomic waste springs from two causes, neither of them indicative of any improvement of man's basic nature.

First, the products of atomic fission were so new, so deadly in minute quantities, and even so "mysterious" that they produced a kind of awe, even among the men who knew most about them. A few pounds of them scattered around might make a continent uninhabitable for five thousand years. They were simply too dangerous to be ignored.

Second, the atomic "business" originally was, and remains, monopolistic at the national level. There are, at present, only five participants—the United States, the Soviet Union, Great Britain, France, and China. We would expect monolithic organization in the two Communist countries, but it seems to be equally strong in the three democracies. One reason is that it all began as "the bomb," a war measure. Besides, the stakes were too high for private enterprise, and government financing was necessary. As earlier chapters in this book should already have shown, an axiom in disposal is that the fewer the sources are, the easier is the solution.

In such a country as the United States, the atomic power plants will soon become, comparatively speaking, common. They will never, however, become as numerous as automobiles, or even as numerous as factories. Moreover, from the beginning, they have operated, and they will continue to operate, under unified and national control.

In the future, increasingly, atomic power plants together with laboratories and some industrial processes, will produce highly dangerous and long-enduring atomic waste. Fortunately, it will be of comparatively small bulk, nothing to compare with sewage and even with garbage. The radioactivity of some of this material declines rapidly, but other parts of it may be considered essentially permanent.

This material is, in many ways, like any other kind of refuse. There is no actually annihilating it. It must be "committed" to air, water, or earth. Obviously, the air is highly unsuitable, and the whole crisis about atomic-testing arose because the waste was being committed to the air. Water also is unsuitable, at least in the sense that the atomic waste should merely be run into water, even as large a body of water as the combined oceans. Sealed into concrete tanks, atomic wastes may be dropped into the depths of the ocean, but even in this case there is the question of whether a concrete tank will endure for more than a few hundred years.

Atomic wastes, therefore, will probably have to be committed to the land. They may be buried in desert basins, where there is little chance that they can pollute the underground water. For additional safety, they may be enclosed in concrete or steel tanks, before being buried. Such areas would have to be enclosed and set aside with access forbidden, like vast charnel-houses.

One advantage of thus disposing of these materials on the land would be that they could be recovered, if any mistake had been made. If a buried tank broke or sprung a leak, its contents could be retrieved. If a tank should break or spring a leak at a depth of a thousand fathoms in the sea, there would be no retrieval. Moreover, there exists at least the possibility that at some future time these materials might prove to be valuable, and there would be a possibility of recovery for recycling.

Inevitably, if civilization continues over the course of centuries, the level of radiation will rise. Inevitably, there will be uncontrolled releases—by human error, by natural catastrophe, or even by malice. But, again, let us not encroach upon the prerogative of the prophets.

14

WASTE WITHOUT WEIGHT

BEGINNING WITH SUCH ANCIENT and natural products as dead bodies and human excreta, and progressing to such sophisticated materials as radioactive waste, the present treatise might well be thought to have covered the field. The topic, however, is essentially too vast and too complicated for any single method of classification, and certain phases of it have slipped through the here-employed net of logic. Sometimes a special problem escaped attention because its introduction at the logical point would have necessitated such a digression as to obscure and impede the general argument. Sometimes the question was one of minor and specialized nature, though not lacking importance, and interest in its place.

For instance, what becomes of the chemicals used for the de-icing of roads? What becomes of the tons of rubber that disappear in the course of a year from millions of tires?

Moreover, some whole aspects of the topic have not appeared in the discussion, which has assumed that everyone was a more-or-less sane and properly functioning individual. Malicious release of noxious matter has so far not gone much beyond dumping detergent into fountains, but the possibility exists. A perverted individual with some energy and a little chemical or biological know-how could poison a whole city's water supply—or perhaps, as a practical joke, render it nauseating and unpalatable.

So also there exists the possibility of accident—the pulling of the wrong lever or the pushing of the improper button. Recently newspapers reported the inadvertent flow of poison from an oil-refinery, and the resulting death of thousands of fish in a large bay.

The present chapter will treat, though briefly, a still different phase or dimension of the general topic. To this point the story has limited itself wholly to the disposal of materials, whether solid, liquid, or gaseous. There has been continued emphasis upon the Conservation of Matter. But refuse, in a larger sense, may be immaterial, as with the no-longer-wanted manifestations of heat and sound, and with what may be termed psychological waste.

. . .

Civilization is dependent upon the production of power. Everywhere except within the tropics, it is also dependent upon the production of a so-called artificial climate by means of what the experts term "space-heating," which the ordinary person merely calls "heating," and, in modern terms, associates with radiators and steam-pipes. To produce and provide space-heating, a city releases enough heat to make its air a degree or two warmer than that of the surrounding country. Even in the highly developed United States, however, such artificial heat equals only an inconsiderable fraction of what the three million square miles within the national boundaries receive from the sun and radiate off into space again, to maintain a heat balance. Man-made heat, therefore, probably creates no cosmic problem, though whatever effect it might have would be to enhance the greenhouse effect of the atmospheric carbon dioxide, and slightly to hasten the melting of the polar ice.

Locally, in the vicinity of large cities, waste heat creates a summertime nuisance, even though production of heat is much reduced at that time. The acute heat problem, however, is that of hot water, and its concentration in the natural drainage.

Many factories use water for cooling, as a part of their processes of production. The water is taken from a stream, at its natural temperature. Some of it may be boiled away in being used as a coolant, and so, having become vapor, is committed to the atmosphere, where it probably does no harm. But most of the water, having cooled the product, has necessarily become warmer, and it is then customarily run out into the stream. Such water, biologically, is unobjectionable. In fact, heating is one way to kill waterborne disease organisms. Accordingly, the public-health authorities pay no attention.

But warm water, poured in large quantities into a stream, can be as deadly as cyanide to many fish and water plants. Subjected to the hot outflow of a steel mill, a pleasant river becomes a desert waste. The effects may extend downstream for many miles and alter the life cycles in the larger rivers.

Atomic power plants, so beneficial with respect to smog, raise a problem of heat by producing immense amounts of hot water. (Sometimes, indeed, one would think that a solution of waste in one area only creates another elsewhere.) When an atomic power plant was proposed for Bodega Point in California, one of the attacks upon it was based upon the problem of disposal. Even granting that the coolant-water would contain no radioactive materials, still it would be warmer than was natural. Though the water would be poured into the Pacific Ocean itself, the largest of all earthly disposal ponds, still there seemed to be some likelihood that the shoreline life would be affected. In the end the building of the plant at this site was abandoned, principally for other reasons, but the problem raised by the production of heat had been recognized and argued.

In the future the question must be faced. As usual there are various expedients, all of them costing money in one way or another, and so constituting a charge upon the production of power. Must the water be temporarily impounded until it radiates its heat off? Must it be artificially cooled? Must the life of the beaches and nearer reefs be sacrificed, with accompanying economic and recreational loss? Must pipelines be constructed to take the effluent sufficiently far to sea? . . .

In a practical way, hot water is now being considered as a waste product in itself, even though the heat that it carries is not a material. The situation with sound, however, is different.

Unlike the purposeful production of heat, the production of sound is nearly all haphazard and incidental. There are exceptions, as when man and other creatures communicate by sound, whether in formal language or by mere cries. Music, also, is purposefully created. So also, such devices as sirens, bells, whistles, and buzzers, send forth auditory signals, which are a sort of extension of language. One might add some other examples, but sound in general, whether natural or artificial, seems to be essentially "waste."

The waves slap on the beach, but the noise seems scarcely to be the occasion for the waves, any more than the rustling of the wind in the leaves seems to justify either the wind or the leaves. The lightning does the real work, and the thunder is just what is left over, though it may have helped primitive man to shape a mythology and even a religion.

There is, indeed, a certain pleasure that many people, on occasion, derive from the creation of sound, as when they set off firecrackers. Probably this springs merely from the sense of power thus derived, since the loud noise in itself may be even painful. In similar fashion sound is pleasantly associated with power in the use of firearms and engines, and certain people build up their egos by gunning their motorboats and by by-passing the mufflers on their automobiles. In general, however, noise is like sin in having very few acknowledged supporters. A survey of the advertisements of any magazine will reveal merchandisers who are promoting sales by announcements of "noiseless"—that is, "less noisy"machines.

Noise, in fact, is one of the great dominating and unwanted monsters that modern civilization has produced. One of the greatest contrasts that we would notice, if transported in time to a city of some centuries ago, would be the unaccustomed, and therefore almost terrifying, silence. Shakespeare, working at a manuscript, would have had as disturbances only the minute scratching of his pen, occasional human voices, the clunk of a horse's hoof on a cobblestone, the yelp of a dog, perhaps a distant sound of trumpets. In contrast, a modern Shakespeare has to cultivate a mind superior to the beating and pounding of traffic on land and in the air, to the roaring of radio and TV, to the whirr of the furnace-fan or of the air-conditioner, probably to not-too-distant blasting, and to the hum of his own electric typewriter and the clatter of its keys.

New inventions ignore the problem of noise, and then refine it out as they develop. The early automobile was noisy, and at one stage of its progress advertisements for the "silent" car were in vogue. After a while the automobile was reduced to a noise-level that was apparently acceptable to most people, and there it stopped. The automobile, however, could still profit by reduction of noise, and the comparative noiselessness of the electric car will be an extra dividend that it will bring.

The early planes, also, were noisy, and conversation on the first air-transports was nearly impossible. As with the automobile, the noise-level was gradually reduced, until it reached an acceptable level—at least one that could be endured without great hardship during a few hours of flight.

The latest threat of noise, and the most critical present one, may be the low-hovering helicopter, but is more likely to be the so-called sonic boom. Modern warfare has necessitated such high-speed planes, and their elimination from military use can be accomplished only by the elimination of war itself. But the development of supersonic transports for civilian traffic seems to be more motivated by senseless national rivalry than by need or demand. What are people going to do that is so important with those few hours saved in the flight from New York to London? Besides, they will have to take time off to get the physical "time-clock" back into running order. Probably such flights, with their accompanying sonic booms will have to be limited to oceanic routes. . . .

Unlike heat and sound, light can scarcely be held to produce a waste problem. Too bright lights, and flashing lights, generally for advertising, are often a nuisance, but such light is produced purposefully, and its brightness is, from the point of view of the producer, a useful quality.

Light-borne, however, are all offensive sights. Mere ugliness is rarely produced for a purposive end and may be held to be a problem of refuse. It is, in fact, being more and more so considered, and attempts to "beautify," though often questionable in themselves, have much the same justification as the attempt to eliminate the effects of hot water or excessive noise.

The chief trouble is that the idea of beauty varies with different people, according to background and accepted conventions and even, perhaps, according to innate character. Moreover, the whole aesthetic conception, as most people have inherited it from the nineteenth century, is in question with many moderns. "Beauty" is no longer the supreme good among architects, painters, sculptors, and musicians. Even modern poets scarcely think of themselves as creating the beautiful.

In the present world the problem probably can be approached better, not as one of beauty in itself, but as one of disorder and impermanency. Such qualities, along with the suggestion of death, may create the shock that the ordinary person feels at the sight of a monstrous heap of abandoned automobile-hulks. A car should be standing on its own four wheels, parked somewhere on a street or in a garage, or else it should be moving along some street or highway, again upon its own four wheels. But in and upon the heap is only a frightful confusion of cars one upon another, lying on their sides or even on their tops, with their bottoms exposed and their wheels abnormally in the air. An aesthetician would be hard put to it to say just why, or even whether, the whole heap is ugly. In fact, its varied and muted colors, flecked with shadows and dwindling off in a fine effect of perspective, might even cause a modern artist to set up his easel. But to the ordinary person the evocative effect is disturbing and is often downright unpleasant. So it comes about that such words as "monstrous" and "frightful" naturally slip into the description of such a modern phenomenon.

Reinforcing the "ugliness" of disorder is that of impermanency. These abandoned cars are too vivid a reminder that all things mundane must pass away. On one day a few years past, the father drove that new car home. Wife and children gazed upon its shiny glamor with eyes of, almost, adoration. The neighbors came, and admired. Then it started on the road, to this town or to that one, as it might happen, but in any case on the well-paved highway to final discard. It suffered its first scratch, its first dented fender. The lacquer dulled a little, the chrome developed a film of dirt. After a while, the engine did not sound the same. The children thought of it as "that old heap," and soon it was traded in. In the next owner's hands it grew more scarred, grimy, and noisy. As its next-to-final halting-place it reached, and in only a few years, this disorderly pile. And then the furnaces!

What we may call the ugliness of disorder and impermanency seems to be the psychological refuse-product of modern civilization.

A glittering beer can at the side of the highway is not ugly in itself, but it is not where it makes any sense by being. The highway iself, swinging around the hills in perfectly adjusted curves, is even a thing of beauty. But, to accommodate it, the outlines of the hills themselves have been violently slashed and disordered, altered from the natural gradients which centuries of rain and growth have established. Attempts to conceal the damage, by planting trees and flowering bushes, are laudable, but they are also admissions of the problem and attempts to retrieve something of what has already gone wrong.

The reference to planting trees and bushes suggests one of the greatest and most pervasive of what may be called the disorders. At some time in the future our present time may well be called The Era of Raw Earth.

Over most of the United States the earth, normally and traditionally, has its layer of soil on top, and this layer is well covered by growth of grass, bushes, or trees. Chiefly where a stream cut through were our ancestors conscious of uncovered subsoil and rock. Now, in what can only be called an unnatural state of disorder, we live upon a largely "skinned" earth. Areas filled with rubble, awaiting their transformation into subdivisions, scarcely support a growth of weeds. Where streets and roads have been put through, the bare surface stands exposed. Occasionally— upon the more important highways—some effort is made to get greenness started again. Too often, not! We are left, again, with the sense of things as they never were before, and as they should not be. One need not write sentimentally about "exposing the bones of Mother Earth." But there arises, inevitably, that sense of disorder. The ordinary citizen has been used to the situation throughout his life, and one may question whether he is adversely affected. But perhaps he is. There is at least a likelihood that the general disorder makes him the more thoughtless about adding his beer can, as what seems to him an infinitesimal and negligible contribution to the already lacerated landscape. There is also the possibility that the apparent acceptance of disorder as a part of his civilization leads him to accept disorder as a natural state of affairs in his own life and in his relations to society.

Impermanency is linked with disorder—especially because the modern American, subjected to violent change beyond his own desire or volition, necessarily tends to see the new as the disordered. A subdivision may be highly structured and even neat, but a man may see it as an unaccustomed invader of the land that he knew as a cornfield or a cow pasture.

American civilization—the most rapidly developing of any in history—has subjected its individuals to conditions of change that no people in the world have ever experienced before, except under the catastrophes of warfare, which we would consider "abnormal." As a mere "normal" by-product, however, our civilization subjects its people to destruction and destruction again, such as not even the hordes of Tamerlane could accomplish. His Tartars killed and burned and perhaps even overthrew walls and filled ditches, but they left the hills and the streams and valleys. Today we tear the hill with a bulldozer, over-whelm the valley with garbage, and degrade the stream into a sewer. Like any other species, man is necessarily conservative, needing a base of ordered solidity. The dif-ference between the so-called "radical" and the so-called "conservative" is really at the superficial level of politics. Actually they both cling about equally to building the futures of their lives upon the established habits of their already-experienced years.

In its treatment of the individual himself, civilization (if we may employ again the abstract term) is callous. It subjects him particularly to change of place. He is a rare fellow, now, who lives out his years in one metropolitan district—or even in one state. In pursuit of immediate "opportunity," at the dictates of a government bureau or a large corporation, he may shift from Nebraska to Califor-nia, and back to Michigan. Realtors flourish confidently, in the knowledge that the average occupancy of a "home," in many districts, is only five years. One may question, under such circumstances, whether anything like a home in the traditional sense of the word can exist at all.

The disorder and impermanency of modern life may not be all for the bad. Some individuals may thus flourish. Change may be stimulating. The same also should have been true for the survivors who came down from the hills and started rebuilding, after Tamerlane's men had passed on. If contemporary American society were free of prob-lems, one would have more confidence in the system.

This subject, however, can only be suggested here, not fully explored. It involves the complexly ramifying prob-lem of the individual in relation to his society, and this book is primarily concerned with the physical refuse, not the psychic waste, of civilization.

The analogy, however, seems to have some validity. The problems bred by disorder and quick change have many resemblances to those of refuse. No one, for instance, sets out purposefully to pollute the streams or to poison the air. Instead, he performs an action which is, by the stan-dards of society, natural and even laudable. When fin-ished, he then discards his refuse.

In similar fashion, no one sets out to destroy land-marks, create confusion, and subject children to the or-deal of changing playmates every few years. It is all part of a system which has its economic ends in view, and must subordinate to those ends the comfort and mental adjustment of the indvidual. By moving him to a new job the corporation, in fact, usually pays him more money. As in polluting the stream and poisoning the air, the basic action is normal and even laudable. No one considers the effect of the wastage. Finally, perhaps, it may force itself on society by such mechanisms as juvenile delinquency, and "nervous breakdown." So also, no one paid attention to what was run into the streams until they became foul.

15

MOMENT OF DECISION

IF SUPER-INTELLIGENT BEINGS are already scouting us, observing our puny efforts from Flying Saucers or other Unidentified Flying Objects, their anthropologists may already have written a report with some such concluding words as these:

> That civilization, therefore, is essentially to be considered as a kind of uncontrolled and inadvertent experiment. No one involved with it has any idea where it is going or how long it will last. Moreover, that civilization gives every impression of being non-reversible and accelerating. One can make only one assumption—that it will continue to go faster and faster in the same general direction, and then it will crash, probably within a century.

More and more of the thinking participants in this civilization seem also to be subscribing to such a view, though usually they keep silent about it. There are simply too many threats. Any one of these—more likely, several of them working together—may prove to be the mechanism. But, as those hovering observers will doubtless conclude eventually, "Civilization was essentially self-destructive, and by its very nature a temporary phenomenon."

War (whether atomic or not), over-population, race and nationality, incompatible political traditions, failure of food-supply, newly-evolved disease organisms, exhaustion of certain natural resources, genetic deterioration in an over-protective society, social alienation—and also the problem of disposal—civilization can scarcely be lucky enough to escape them all, especially since one will set another into action, like the often-mentioned row of falling dominoes.

If civilization is thus non-reversible and accelerating, destined for a not-too-distant smash, no one needs to be too much worried about a few loose beer cans. Indeed, one of the survivors, as he goes scavenging about, will be happy to discover an occasional can, left unvaporized.

Still, prophecy is a tricky trade, and prophets must be especially chary about setting time-limits. Civilization is a large affair, and in such masses the movement is always likely to be slower than one expects. In short, not only may the whole idea of a crashing end be wrong, but also, even granting that end, the time remaining may amount to several centuries. Certainly, the general premises of our life do not assume a quickly approaching end.

The question of refuse disposal should therefore move to a high place among the concerns of civilized man. Mere accumulation of wastes with resulting deterioration of the environment—even its actual poisoning—may become the critical element in man's fate.

There seems to be no possibility that the problem will simply go away of itself. As outlined in an early chapter, the recent causes are four—increase in population, urbanization, affluence, and new materials. There is every indication that the population of the United States will continue to increase—at least throughout the next generation. Cities will therefore grow larger. In spite of competition for materials from the emergent nations, affluence will increase, nationally, though with increased population certain groups may not share in it. As a part of affluence, many new and highly non-degradable materials will be produced in large quantities. Concomitantly, we thus have reason to believe, the production in waste materials will accelerate and the increase will have to be measured yearly in millions of tons—solids, liquids, and gases. . . .

As at present seen, and as projected into the near future, two aspects of the disposal problem appear to be the most dangerous.

First, the mass production of some violent poison may do the work—quickly perhaps, or by cumulative effect. The possibilities already exist, and there is a definite chance that the poisons already poured out into the environment are causing irreparable damage. This damage need not necessarily be directly inflicted upon the human race, but could be a devastation produced somewhere in the environment, which would only manifest itself in the life of man, eventually, by the setting up of some kind of chain-reaction.

Such a possibility exists because the agents of civilization—that is, civilized men—have worked upon the principle, "Produce first for the immediate 'good' end; consider the consequences later." Or, as it runs in the jargon of the merchandiser, "Enjoy now, pay later."

Within the period of the last single generation of men, three such possibilities have been produced, and are actually with us. We face, not a theory, but a situation, or three situations. First, the users of pesticides have flooded the landscape with subtle, violent, and long-enduring poisons, as lethal to men as to insects and worms. Second, the users of automobiles—that is to say all Americans—have filled the air itself with poisons. Third, the manipulators of atomic processes have produced certain quantities of essentially unnatural and permanent materials the effects of which can be so catastrophic in minute proportions that the conventional word "poison" is scarcely adequate to describe them.

In addition to these obvious three, still other activities of our present civilization may be, even now, producing materials that have not yet been recognized as critical. Almost surely, in the near future, more such will be loosed upon the environment, and at some juncture there may be a passing of some unnoted point of no return.

We need not, however, think merely in terms of a dramatic catastrophe. The second general possibility for disaster does not involve millions dead in an afternoon, but merely the commonplace and dreary cast-offs of daily living—sewage, garbage, junk, litter, and their associated disorder, impermanency, harsh noises, and bad smells. Civilization, as the phrase goes, may be pecked to death by ducks.

Who can keep his pride, or even his self-respect, when living on top of a garbage-dump? Doubtless a philosopher could do so, as Diogenes is reputed to have done when living in a tub. But few men are philosophers.

Any society, one would think, must give its members something to live by, a certain solidity of the present that implies a future, a certain sense of attending to the immediate problem, as a responsible adult, and not merely throwing it aside, as a small child throws a gum-wrapping, for someone else to consider—and, perhaps, to pick up.

Civilization, therefore, may meet its end, not from the increase of carbon monoxide or some pesticide, but from the decrease of honesty, responsibility, and decency. What is called alienation from society seems to be especially a phenomenon of the last generation. One notes such problems as juvenile delinquency and organized crime. One notes the New Left, with its explicit pride in its alienation, and its unwillingness to formulate, or even to try to formulate, a positive ideology.

To blame such matters directly on improper disposal of garbage would, naturally, be ridiculous. At least, however, the truth is that the phenomenon of alienation has arisen in the same period that has seen the disposal problem become acute. It has, moreover, sprung, obviously, from some of the same sources—from increase of population and its crowding into cities, so that the individual becomes lost in the crowd and faceless, and from an affluence that, for instance, carries insurance against peculation, and so can shrug off the moral issue.

A further danger in the same connection, arises from the mere ability of the human being to get used to situations by a kind of evolutionary adaptation. In a work of science fiction, indeed, one could suggest even physical adjustments. The future Americans might be portrayed as being nearsighted, because the smog cuts off all possibility of distant views anyway. Besides, the continual coursing of tears down their cheeks will have proved, over the ages, to be a biological handicap, and so they have developed tear-bladders, which they can empty at convenient intervals, withdrawing modestly to do so.

Science fiction aside, there now exists in some of our cities a whole generation of individuals, all those under thirty years of age, who have grown up under smog conditions. This, to them, is just the way things are! Presumably they have no desire for clean air because they do not even know what it is. One possibility is that such people will see no reason in taxing themselves or otherwise going to trouble to change matters, by making them somewhat "better," when they do not even know what "better" means. Even the older people in many areas have become so used to smog that they have ceased to be much concerned over it. One begins to wonder if, somewhere in that complex mixture that is smog, there exists a tranquilizer, which produces an apathy to smog itself.

Meanwhile, the life of a city can continue, and people can even live lives of gaiety and culture. The city is so far removed from the basic environment as essentially to ignore it. Like conquerors behind their castle walls, levying tribute upon the peasants, many urbanites look upon the environment merely as something to supply the necessities, including the amusements, that city-people need or think they need. As, perhaps, the conquerors wore the peasants down and were forced, themselves, to live in poverty, so also it may happen with the city-folk. The degradations of the environment cannot continue, progressively, forever. And, in the degradation of the environment, the disposal of refuse has become a major factor.

In general, then, the situation is not good, and in certain respects it is very bad indeed. We may, however, have some confidence in the American people.

That people has faced bad situations before. It is not a people that behaves properly on every occasion, and its philosophers have quite justly taken it to task for various errors and shortcomings. But of one failing it has never been guilty. It has not lain down in apathy when faced with a difficult or dangerous crisis. It has done something, and there is plenty of evidence at the present time that it is getting ready to do something again.

As to what needs to be done and must be done, this book has so far made only proposals in detail. Actually, however, the whole problem is one. What should be done, as is true in many large issues, is clear enough in a general way, however difficult the practical implementation.

First, must come education—and not merely the shifting of the problem to the already overworked classroom teacher. Education must be general and at all levels, and the chief function of such a book as this must be considered educational. In a democracy, indeed, we fortunately lack a state-directed Department of Propaganda, but by that lack the problem of general education becomes more difficult. In a situation such as this we must depend upon somewhat haphazard means of shaping public opinion. But it has been done in other situations, and can probably be done in this one.

Education is necessary, most obviously, in connection with such a problem as litter, where the cooperation of the individual is essential. But also it is necessary because great amounts of public money must be spent, and the public must know the necessity, and also what it is getting in return—which is the continuing life of American civilization.

We should not underestimate the possibilities of education. So far, one can scarcely say that it has even been tried. If any considerable fraction of the money now spent on advertising beer were to be spent in educating people about litter, the results might be as spectacular as the present sales of beer.

Education should also be directed at the economists themselves, since those specialists have as yet paid almost no attention. Both in theory and in practice, disposal should be integrated with business, as a necessary part of the whole economic cycle.

Second, comes the need for more research, not only in the highly complex scientific and engineering problems, but also in even the rather simple matters of statistics.

How little is at present known even in a gross way may be shown by the experience of a recent committee of the National Academy of Sciences which attempted to compile statistical data upon a single region. That which was selected was thought to be the best available for the purpose—the area of the lower Delaware River, a long-established center of American civilization. The study, however, broke down. Even in such an area the necessary statistics were simply not available—what might be called a failure at a primary level. Very much more difficult are the scientific and technical problems to be solved.

The fact is that no one knows at the present time how some of these problems are to be solved at all, much less how they are to be solved within practical financial limits, and in time. As compared with any of the individual bills of many billions to improve a single phase of the situation, any money spent upon research is a minor expense, almost certain to repay itself a hundred times over. The amount spent could be doubled or tripled at once, and might be multiplied many times over, in future years, as greater numbers of properly trained personnel become available. And the honor of these men in their land should be high.

Jonathan Swift, in a noble and often-quoted passage written two centuries ago, declared that a man who made two blades of grass to grow where only one grew before deserved more of his country than the whole race of politicians. His emphasis upon increased production was typical of his time and country—even more so of twentieth-century America. But now we are arriving at a time of overproduction when we might well revise the passage. "He who discovers how to get rid of two tin cans where only one was got rid of before deserves better of his country than the whole race of advertisers."

Third, a considerable reorganization at the political or administrative level is necessary.

Disposal-products are not only massive in bulk. Also, for such a massive tonnage, they are curiously mobile. Committed to winds, streams, and currents, they respect neither city limits nor county boundaries. They cross state lines just as readily, and even do not halt before the flags of Canada and Mexico.

As a regional problem, the handling of refuse demands organization into districts based upon environmental units, not upon some whim of past history that drew an arbitrary boundary line, east-west, or north-south. Hundreds of independent and almost sovereign municipalities, communities, counties, and states, cannot continue, without higher direction, to dump indiscriminately into the same river or bay.

A somewhat typical American situation occurs in the already-mentioned natural geographical unit of the lower Delaware River. As things go in the United States, it is not a large area—only 4,600 square miles. But in 1964 the governmental functions, including that of disposal, were fractionated among three states, eleven counties, and 377 municipalities.

Zoning regulations within cities seem now to have established themselves. Equally, or more, we need zoning at the state level, to attain some rational and long-enduring development in harmony with the environment. Thus we might escape such insanities as what amounts, in one instance, to a government subsidy to enable half a million more people to move into a region already in a crisis because of smog.

Eventually, and by the same reasoning, we need something in the nature of national zoning to prevent one state becoming crowded beyond natural capacities for good living, through a kind of insensate economic gravitational force by which people attract more people. Such a process also leaves other areas in the decadence that results from a declining population and from economic contraction.

Also at the national level, therefore, the environment must have recognition, and there has recently been much indication to that effect. The work of President Johnson's Science Advisory Committee is notable, and in 1965 its Environmental Pollution Panel released a 317-page basic and excellent report, with the significant title *Restoring the Quality of Our Environment*. That title, indeed, might be criticized as more exact than catchy, but its words must have been carefully chosen, and the emphasis upon quality and restoration are noteworthy.

Of similar significance, at the national level, is the 257-page report of the Federal Council for Science and Technology, appearing in 1966 under the title *Waste Management and Control*.

Aside from support in the battle against particular phases of the problem, a possibility at the national level would be a cabinet post, Secretary of the Environment. Such a department would absorb certain duties of presently-functioning departments, especially that of Health, Education and Welfare. In taking over the field of "Health," however, it would cease to consider the area as concerned merely or chiefly with human medical problems, and would be involved with ecology, the environment as a whole, its capacity to maintain, now and in the future, a prosperous, vigorous, and happy people. . . .

Just as the question of what should be done, in the larger aspects, is simple enough, so also the question of how it should be done seems to be easy, theoretically.

Only two basic methods of disposal exist, and they may be called roughly, "dumping," and "recycling."

Dumping is natural and primitive. It is often the simplest and the cheapest method—at least, in its immediate cost—and it will undoubtedly be with us always. In the water and in the air this dumped material is so widely diffused that it is essentially lost forever, though it has devastating results. Material dumped on the land is theoretically recoverable. Such dumping, however, reduces the much-needed space for human life, and becomes psychologically depressive.

Civilized man will never, probably, escape from the necessity of a certain amount of dumping. Some used materials—broken dishes furnish a good example—are highly durable, incorruptible, and without value. Such leavings, if heavier than water, can be safely dumped into even the shallower parts of the ocean. In general, however, dumping is essentially an unsophisticated method for savages and primitive villagers, who have plenty of space and tolerant noses. Civilized man should try for something better.

Recycling is the only other basic method. Even some apparent dumping may be called recycling, as when demolition products from one site furnish fill for another site. The trouble here is that the need to dump sometimes takes precedence, as when contractors eagerly seize upon the opportunity to fill a marsh, without any consideration of whether the marsh—as a needed link in a biological chain should be preserved for its wildlife.

Recycling includes all methods of disposal which have as a definite end the return of the material to "use." That term has to be defined as human use, directly or indirectly, since even philosophers seem to recognize no other ultimate good in the world.

The methods of recycling differ basically in how far the material is allowed to return to a simpler state before it is again put to use. Several different degrees can be noted. Collected bottles, for instance, are taken merely as they are, and are then washed, sterilized, and refilled. Scrap metal has to go farther around, being melted down and then re-structured, usually into something wholly different. At a further remove still, manure is spread upon the fields, aids the growth of crops, and thus returns. Finally, such materials as prunings must be piled up, allowed gradually to return to simpler materials by the process of decay, and then finally returned as plant growth.

Rather obviously, the ideal should be recycling. Especially, it should be a kind of recycling that does not put the material out of circulation for a long time, thus to produce "unemployment" of matter along with environmental clutter. An example would be the method, with sewage, by which it is not sent the long way around via agriculture, but is shortcutted into new food materials in a pond.

In the large sense, then, what we should do with waste materials seems clear. But recycling might be described as a good trick when you can work it. In actual practice the procedures are infinitely complicated, economically dubious, and impeded by tradition and custom, sometimes reaching the intensity of taboo. . . .

The removal of the causes or sources of refuse—prevention rather than cure—would also seem to be a natural approach. Two of the four basic causes, population and urbanization, if they are controllable at all, will not be controlled merely for the purpose of alleviating the disposal problem. On the other hand, the control and even restriction of the production of new materials has already been to some extent practiced, and will have to become commoner.

Most interesting of all is the relationship of affluence to disposal. As so often emphasized, affluence is one of the chief causes. At the same time, it may well be in the long run one of the chief agencies in combating improper disposal. As already pointed out, affluent people have time to enjoy their environment and therefore to object to its degradation.

Prevention rather than cure should, however, be the approach in certain phases of the problem, such as litter. With others, such as smog, it is, apparently, the only approach possible.

Closely allied to prevention is what might be called "close-up" retrieval. Factory effluents and smoke, for instance, are obviously much better handled by being collected before they leave the factories; in fact, there is scarcely any other way. In a somewhat analogous manner the phases of the problem involving individuals, such as junk and litter, might be better solved by moving the point of attack close to the individual himself, not only by trying to change his psychology, but also by supplying better means for him to pass his refuse on, and even a slight financial motive.

The present work, however, an essay and not an exhaustive treatise, must renounce the duty or privilege of specific recommendations. A whole series of such may be profitably studied in one section of *Restoring the Quality of our Environment*.

16

IN PRAISE OF SHIVA

In a concluding chapter the attention may turn to larger aspects. What is the worldwide significance? What are the complexities of the social situation? What even is "good"?

That the crisis of disposal is worldwide should already be clear enough from passing comments in preceding chapters. Lake Constance, on the borders of Switzerland and Germany, is in a comparable state of pollution to Lake Tahoe on the borders of California and Nevada. The air is close to being lethal and threatening, not only in Los Angeles and New York, but also in London, throughout the valley of the Meuse in Belgium, and in Osaka and Tokyo. Crowded England, even more than the United States, is suffering from the abandonment of old cars along the roads.

Throughout those large areas that are sometimes ironically known as the "civilized" world, the four basic causes of the overproduction of refuse are at work. Even the mushrooming cities of the underdeveloped nations, though notably lacking in affluence, are oppressed by the problem of sewage disposal produced by crowding of people.

We, the civilized people of the world, have come to the end of an era. We have not been arboreal for a million or two years, and we must at last renounce the arboreal assumption that the way to get rid of something is to let it drop. We have run out of space.

In this negative aspect of civilization, however, as in so many of the positive aspects, the United States must be conceded the leadership, chiefly because its people enjoy more affluence.

As to what the Americans, this most affluent people in the world, are minded to do about this problem, the answer is not altogether clear, as yet. They have, so to speak, been able to live beyond their means by over-drawing the bank account. Are they ready now to correct this situation by so many billions of taxes and other charges that some restriction of the individual affluence may result?

Theoretically the answer would appear to be yes. In some phases of the problem—smog, for instance—absolute necessity would seem to give no choice. But even here we cannot be certain. The question already raised with respect to smog may be here raised again with respect to disposal in general. Have people merely got used to it? Will they continue sweeping the material under the rug or piling it in a corner of the room? Will the cities merely sacrifice the countryside?

The American citizen of the future—and possibly of the near future—may be content to breathe purified air, not pure air, just as he now may drink purified water, not pure water. Whole city blocks are even now, occasionally, being insulated and air-conditioned. The future citizen may venture into the "open air," only to pass through it, perhaps with the aid of a mask, and so to reach another air-conditioned haven. As for the bad effect of smog on agriculture, that will be minimized because most of the basic food will be produced from sewage-ponds. As for running streams, they will merely exist to carry away sewage and factory effluents. The land itself, for miles around each city, will be a garbage dump.

With the air-conditioned areas, the arts and sciences will flourish mightily, and the mass media will keep every-one much amused and very happy. Disneyland and Las Vegas, and their many successors, will supply infinite escape, and colored TV will offer tales of covered wagons and Indians that will yearly move farther from the tenu-ous reality that they now retain.

To millions of people in the United States, perhaps to a majority of them, such a picture probably offers nothing of horror, would seem quite possible of achievement in not too many years, and would be accepted as a fine way of life. In fact, even at the present time, many city-dwellers have thus isolated themselves from the natural environment. Such people are not merely those of the slums, but they include many people who consider them-selves (and are generally so considered by others) as the highest development of modern civilization.

In the face of such opposition or indifference, the whole

approach of the present volume may have been fallacious. It has assumed what may in the future be considered an early-twentieth-century attitude, that the mess should be cleaned up. The later-twentieth-century attitude may be that you should merely isolate yourself from the mess.

In the long run the attitude of isolation will not work. It may work for a generation, however, and during that time it will be cheaper than the other approach. A generation may be all that civilization needs. . . .

Another factor exists in the situation, and it is a curious one. In most people's minds the problem of disposal is tied up with such movements as conservation and beautification. Certainly, there are points of contact. Those movements, however, seem to be constantly in opposition to a powerful but somewhat vague entity known as "business." Those interested in decent disposal, on the other hand, are not in opposition to "business," and should even find in it their most enthusiastic ally.

If billions of dollars must be expended, the economic opportunity is magnificent. New machines, complicated processes, massive enterprises of transportation, must be developed, marketed, and maintained. Millions of men must be employed. Possibly as much creative energy can be put to work in recycling things as in originally producing them. In this connection, therefore, we need not even renounce our worship of "production," as the essential good.

The title *Not So Rich As You Think* has emphasized this economic aspect of the topic. Such emphasis is well warranted. At the end, however, we may pass, for a moment, into an even more basic, though not unrelated field—that of religion.

Judaism and Christianity, we may maintain, whether shaping Western civilization or shaped by it, present a philosophy of production, and are thus in harmony with that civilization. Those predominant Western religions conceive God as the Creator—an epithet, that some modern version might render and, for all I know, may already have rendered, as the Producer.

Far back, in the small print and the footnotes of theology, there is, indeed, what is known as eschatology, a consideration of how things are going to end. There seems to be some indication that Jehovah is also the Destroyer, who intends to finish off the world that he once created. The theologians appear to be a little shamefaced about this, that their deity should behave in such an un-Creatorlike fashion, and the details are obscure and uncertain. By one account He will destroy the old earth and heaven only to create new ones, though assigning the sea to utter destruction. In any case, each soul is conceived as being created, but never destroyed, thus committing some theologians to the unpleasant but necessary assumption that many of the said souls must burn forever in hell.

Thus, even Western religion assigns the goodness and the glory to creation, which we may call production. And so, let us look at another religion, and to the wisdom of another region. As the title of this chapter proclaims, let us offer, for a moment, our praise to Shiva.

In Hinduism equal share is given to the principle of getting rid of things. Of the great triad, if Brahma is the creator and Vishnu the preserver, Shiva is the destroyer, and his work is held equally essential. In fact, his worshipers assign him first place, pointing out that, being the destroyer, he is also creator. The new can burgeon forth and be young—only after the old has ceased to be.

AUTHOR'S NOTE

As I CONTEMPLATE the finished typescript, this book seems, in some ways, a strange one for me to have written. In deeper ways, however, I can see it is a natural development out of much of my earlier interests and work. In such novels as *Storm* and *Earth Abides*, in *Names on the Land* and other books of non-fiction, I had considered environment and the complex system of human ecology. So does the present book.

I should not, however, have undertaken the work except for the suggestion and prompting of two eminent men. In December, 1965, I received a letter from L. M. K. Boelter (since then, I am sorry to record, deceased), who was at that time Professor Emeritus, and former Dean of the College of Engineering of the University of California at Los Angeles. He urged me to "undertake a book on AIR—it could be considered a sequel to STORM." I replied that I appreciated his confidence, but did not see, at the moment, how I could comply. Shortly afterward, however, I had a similar suggestion from George Maslach, Dean of the College of Engineering of the University of California (Berkeley). He spoke to me personally, and his suggestion was for a book on the whole problem. He assured me that the experts among his colleagues would be glad to cooperate with me.

I could not help being impressed that both these men thought that such a book should be written, and that I should do it, and that help upon technical problems would be available. Moreover, such a book, I could see, should be prepared as a matter of public service, if for no other reason. In short, I finally went ahead with the project.

I must acknowledge essential help from some important recent studies, two of them already mentioned in the text. One of these is *Restoring the Quality of our Environment,* Report of the Environmental Pollution Panel, President's Science Advisory Committee (The White House, November, 1965). Another is *Waste Management and Control,* by the Committee on Pollution, National Academy of Sciences, National Research Council Publication 1400 (Washington, D.C., 1966). A third report, though technically limited to the situation in one state, is of broad general interest, *i.e., California Waste Management Study,* a report to the State of California Department of Public Health, No. 3056, prepared by Aerojet-General Corporation (August, 1965). Useful in their fields have been two books by Donald E. Carr, *viz., The Breath of Life* (1965) and *Death of the Sweet Waters* (1966).

A good deal of current information has been gleaned here and there from magazine articles and from accounts in newspapers. In fact, the bulk of such material in itself demonstrates the present importance of the topic and the general interest in the problem. Paul L. Burton has been especially helpful in supplying clippings from newspapers in Detroit and its vicinity, one of the important centers of activity.

My chief help and reliance has been Percy ("Mac") H. McGauhey. He has been unsparing in his aid and counsel, though the responsibility for both the facts and the opinions remain mine.

I wish also to express my thanks, for aid and cooperation, to my wife, Theodosia Burton Stewart, and to many friends who in one way or another have contributed to the completion of the project.

AUTHOR'S NOTE—1970

FIRST PUBLISHED IN 1968, this book appeared before the national surge of involvement in the environmental crisis. This tremendous and sudden burgeoning of interest is an amazing phenomenon. It has led to the misuse of the old scientific term "ecology" to cover, roughly, the entire movement. To be for this cause has come to be much like being for motherhood or against sin. A few years ago President Johnson, Secretary Udall, Senator Muskie, and a few others were almost lonely advance fighters among thousands of governmental officeholders. In the last two years a dedication to the attack upon pollution has become a required routine for every politician. In 1968 the journalistic space devoted to the subject was negligible; today scarcely an issue of a newspaper appears without half-a-dozen stories. Even various youth movements have taken up the fight, each in its own fashion attempting to save the world from this disaster, but seldom working in conjunction with the Establishment or any other group.

Such a change of attitude may in itself be considered a revolutionary advance. Unfortunately, both politicians and youth groups have accomplished less in actual clean-up than they have in making speeches and statements, jumping on bandwagons, and performing symbolic acts, such as burying a new automobile. These procedures are easier ones than advocating large new taxes, or paying them.

Partly for this reason, the present book has not gone out of date. A more important reason is that it deals with the fundamentals of the worldwide problem, which do not change in a year or two because they are involved with human evolution and history. Therefore, the general principles laid down in Chapter 1 are still applicable; the historical background of Chapter 2 continues to be sound; the four basic causes, as outlined in Chapter 3, remain the same. Moreover, very little of the rest of the book needs to be corrected, though examples drawn from the last two years might be added, together with some reappraisal of opinions. The chapter on agricultural waste, for instance, is probably more optimistic—or, at least, less pessimistic—than now seems warranted, in view of the still-unsolved situation that is being created by continued use of pesticides. Similarly, recent studies have suggested that the open ocean itself may not be too large to be polluted, and that the decimation of plankton from DDT may affect the oxygen-balance of the atmosphere.

The possibility of accident—briefly mentioned in Chapter 14—has assumed new dimensions with the problem of oil-spillage. Even though accident, strictly speaking, is something else than disposal, the general effects are so much the same that their separation is rather of the mind than of the everyday world.

Here and there, in particular details, the situation has improved. In some areas smog is somewhat abated; certain communities have improved their sewage disposal; a few streams are less polluted. But in other areas, communities, and streams, as urbanization and population have continued to increase and as careless affluence has induced an even more acute disposal problem, the situation has further deteriorated. One would have difficulty in establishing the fact of any significant improvement, except in the already-mentioned great arousal of interest.

Moreover, during the time that has elapsed since the first publication, I have, as author, seen no reason to change the thinking upon which were based the ideas, conclusions, and recommendations of the two final chapters. In one respect only does it seem to me that I have advanced or matured that thinking. Disposal now appears to me to be even more closely integrated with the whole set of modern problems, as briefly listed in Chapter 15. To use a military analogy, the United States is forced to fight upon all fronts at once. We cannot, first, solve the racial problem, then go on to take care of poverty, then end war, and perhaps after that loose our tremendous national potential upon the disposal problem. No; not one of these or of the other dangers is going to wait its turn. Instead, each one fights as ally beside the others, so that their total strength is multiplied.

To continue the military analogy, the United States now seems to have only two ready sources of reserve power which could quickly be thrown into the general struggle. The money and manpower that are being employed in Vietnam and in the exploration of space might be turned, without reduction of their forces, toward victory in these other crises. In terminating the space effort now that we are ahead, we should not even lose face. To abandon Vietnam might mean loss of face, and hard times for some of the Vietnamese. But not to do so might mean a loss, not of face, but of our necks, and hard times for a great many people, not only some Vietnamese. We have no reason to think that all of these problems, including pollution, will obligingly wait until we finally find a convenient time to do something.

George R. Stewart

San Francisco, 1970

Index

173